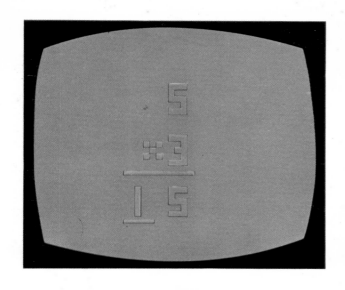
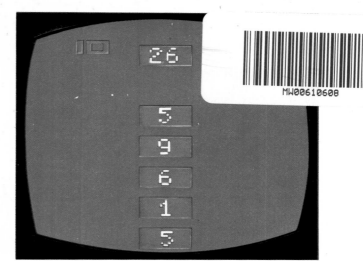

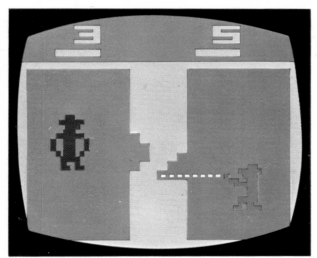
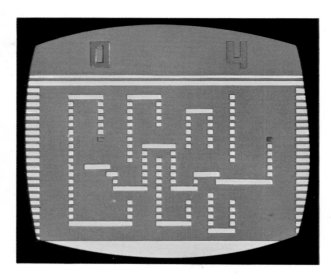

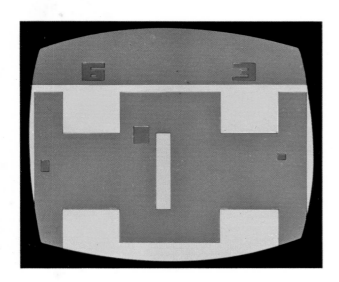
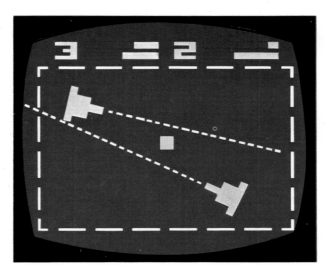

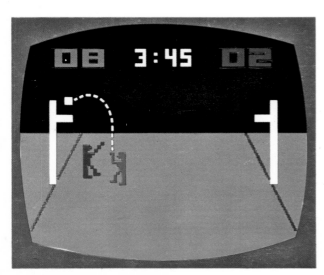
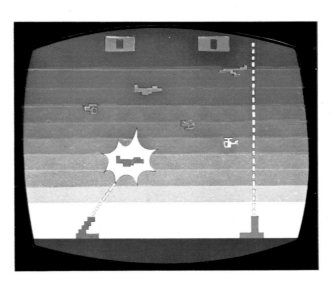

Future
WORLD

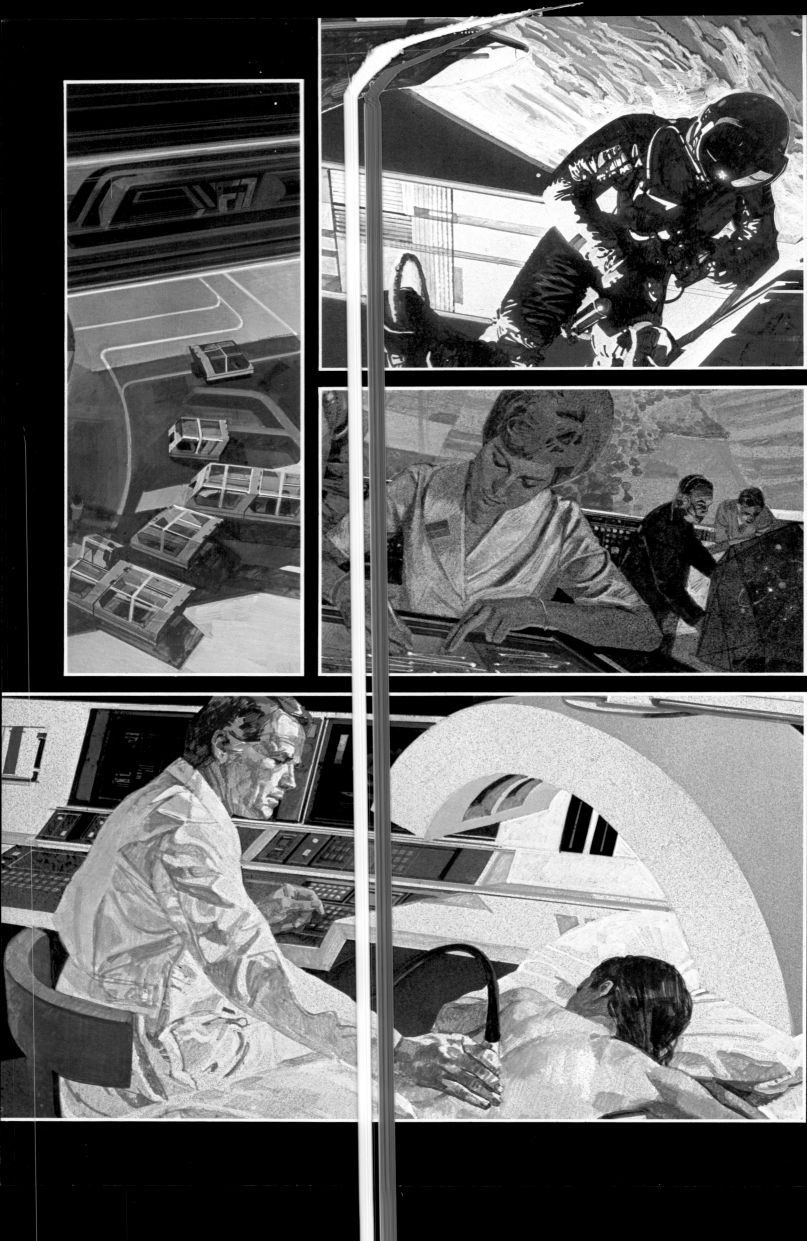

Future
WORLD
Peter Goodwin

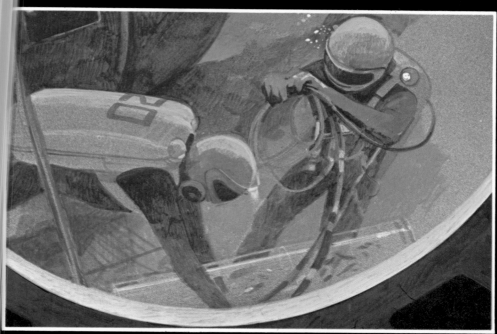

Crescent Books
New York

First published by The Hamlyn Publishing Group Limited
London · New York · Sydney · Toronto
Astronaut House, Feltham, Middlesex, England. 1979

Library of Congress Catalog Card Number: 79–52620

This edition is published by Crescent Books,
a division of Crown Publishers, Inc.

Colour separations by Culver Graphics Limited, Lane End, Buckinghamshire.

Printed in Spain by Graficromo S.A., Córdoba.

Picture research by Angela Murphy.

Contents

Design for Living

At first sight, the cities, towns and villages of the year 2000 may not look very different from the way they do today, but in most developed countries, computer control will bring about great differences in lifestyle, not only in offices, factories and transport systems, but also in the home. In the 1950s, when computers first came into widespread use, a large machine capable of performing complex mathematical tasks, cost hundreds of thousands of dollars. Today, devices having the same capacity, but often with vastly improved facilities, cost only a few hundred dollars. Because of rapidly advancing micro-miniaturisation, the nose-dive of computer prices is continuing, and it is predicted confidently that every company, every office, and every person could soon own a computer capable of performing a vast range of tasks.

The boom in computer power is being fueled by the rapid development and improvement of the tiny devices called chips which form the microscopic but powerful brains of modern computers. Chips are tiny wafers made of the element silicon, onto which are etched complex, printed electronic circuits. They are small enough to pass through the eye of a needle. In the early days of computers, a computer wiring circuit would have filled a large space, but it can now be printed on a single chip. This has been made possible by microscopic photography techniques in which a circuit blueprint is reproduced in full, complex detail on the tiny slice of silicon. More importantly, the same circuit can be reproduced accurately hundreds of thousands of times for cheap mass production of the chips.

At the industrial development nick-named 'Silicon Valley' near San Francisco, California, where four-fifths of the world's chips are now being made, chip manufacturing technology is progressing at a phenomenal rate. Ever more complex and miniaturised circuits are etched on the tiny chips, and it is now estimated that the price of silicon chips will be halved every eighteen months during the next decade or so, making it possible for successive generations of computers to

Above
A 1.495 sq. cm (0.23 sq. in) *silicon chip*, the Ferranti F100—L microprocessor, photographed in the eye of a needle.

Opposite
Enlarged view of a Bell Labs — designed CCD filter showing *silicon chip* features in detail.

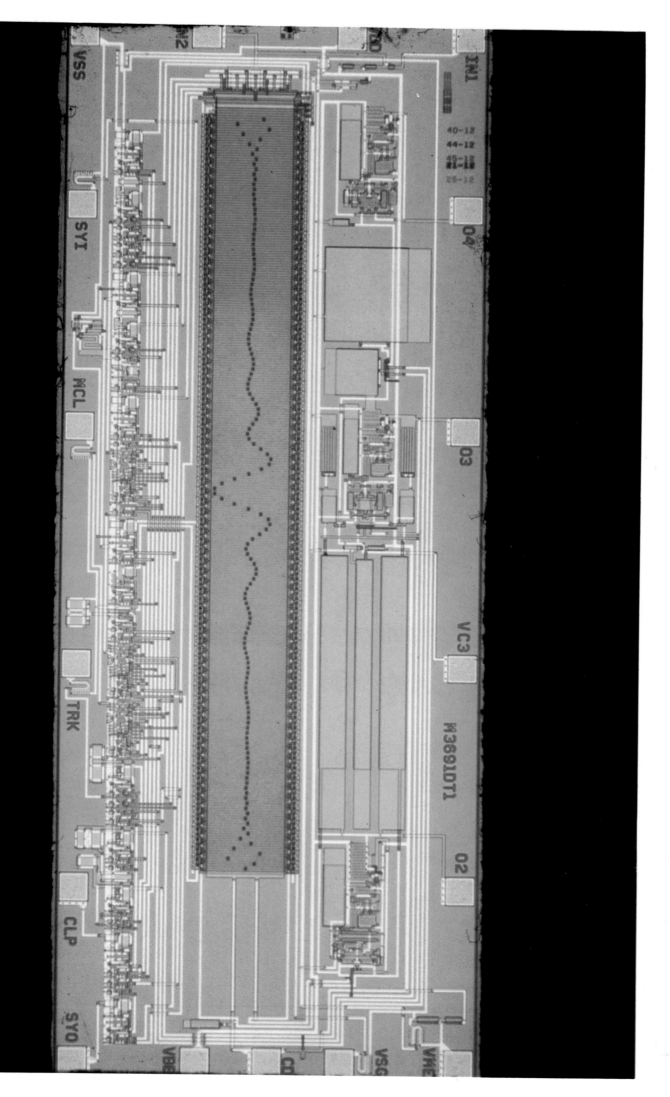

11

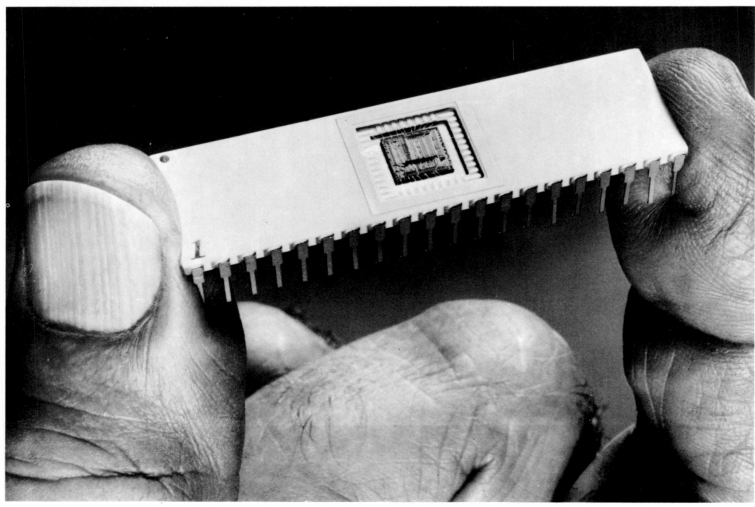

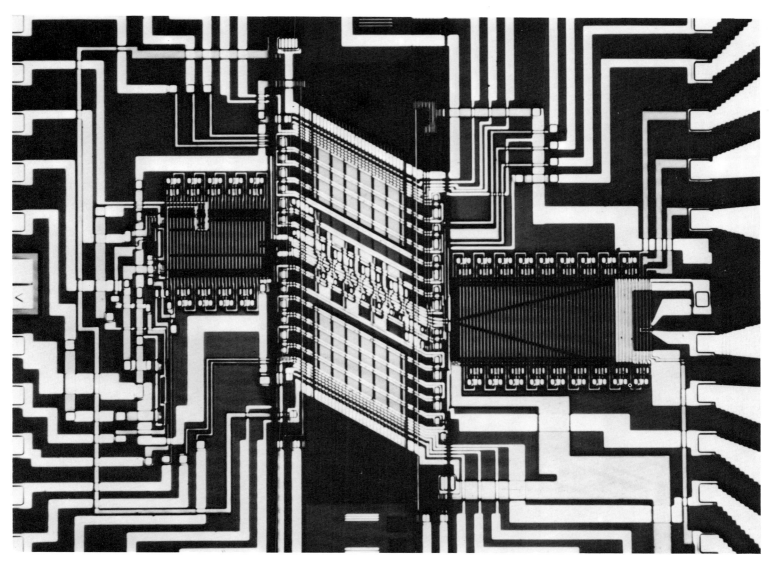

Above
This experimental microcircuit *1K–bit chip (with a magnetic bubble lattice storage device)*, contains all the elements needed to read, write, and store information in a hexagonal array of magnetic bubbles.

In the picture, the storage area appears as a parallelogram which is about 1.6 cm ($\frac{1}{64}$ inch) long on the device itself. The area contains 1,024 information-bearing bubbles arranged in a lattice containing 32 rows and 32 columns. The 5-micron diameter bubbles, whose centres are separated by 11.5 microns, store information at a density of over 5 million bits per square inch. Information is represented by controllable differences in the magnetic structure of the walls.

Halfway across the parallelogram is a pattern of gold conductors that serve as an access channel for the feeding of individual bubbles into and out of the array. The isolated bubbles are generated and encoded in the device's 'write station' (the rectangular area below the lattice), and the information contained in the bubbles is detected in the 'read station', which appears above the lattice.

Opposite top
ITT semiconductors
Circuit diagram for a micro-memory.

Opposite bottom
A Ferranti F100–L *microprocessor chip* mounted in a 40-pin dual-in-line package.

become cheaper and more powerful.

There are different sorts of chips for different purposes within the computer. The thinking and calculating processes are performed by chips called microprocessors which can be used independently of an entire computer to automate mechanical processes. Another important computer circuit now being produced in chip form is the electronic memory. At the beginning of the 1970s, the chips known as Random Access Memories, or RAMs, were capable of storing one thousand characters on a piece of silicon smaller than a finger nail. By the late 1970s, however, the 64K RAM, which could store sixty-four thousand items on a single chip, had been developed. Already, the chip companies are discussing the 256K RAM, and looking to the future, there seems no limit to the ultimate miniaturisation of these computer memory devices. The American company, Texas Instruments, which developed the 64K RAM, predicts that the devices will cost $55 each initially. A year later, the price will have fallen to $38, and the slide will go on until they should cost only $4 each by 1985. In other fields of technology, even marginal reductions of price have led to much greater public demand. In the case of

these miniature computer components, the dramatic fall in prices should make countless new computer applications available to the average person, changing our world drastically.

In the home of the future, door-locks, windows, shutters, domestic appliances, central heating, air conditioning, leisure and education equipment, and just about anything else imaginable, could all be controlled by a miniature computer. For example, a visitor arrives at the front of a house door, presses what looks like the door bell, and waits. He is greeted by a voice coming from a small loudspeaker in the door. This is the voice-response system of a domestic computer that is programmed to analyse and recognise the human voice. By measuring the frequency content of the visitor's voice, the computer can produce a 'voiceprint' that, like a fingerprint, is unique and can identify an individual. Following a response, the domestic computer can open the door to the visitor, or ask him to wait while the householder is consulted.

In the mid 1970s, E.M.I., a British company, developed the first effective speech recognition machine in the world. It was based on the knowledge that all human speech consists of no more than a few dozen basic building blocks

13

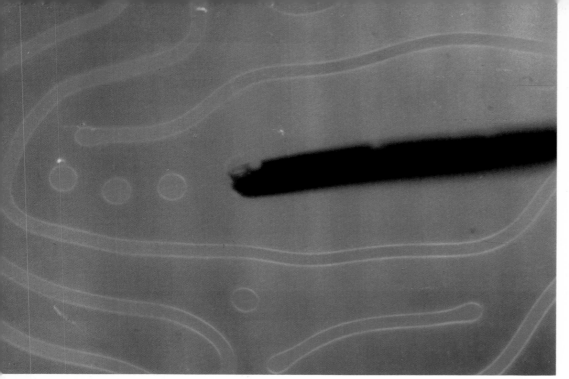

Left
Resembling the ridges and valleys of a finger-print, these tiny red strips are human hair-size *magnetic bubbles*. Scientists at Bell Laboratories have found that they can control features such as memory, logic, counting, and switching, which are vital to computer communications.

Below
This *EMI Threshold Voice Recognition Computer* is the result of a major technological breakthrough. Previously, a computer could function by receiving instructions in its own language only, but now computers can be made to understand any spoken language provided the computer has been trained.

A training session involves the repetition of a word ten times. Each repetition creates a slightly different pattern, representing the speaker's mode of ennunciation. The computer then averages out the variations and selects a single reference pattern for each word. The number of speaker-trainers is limited only by the size of the memory.

After training, the computer identifies a spoken word by measuring accoustic characteristics and comparing them to the pattern stored in its memory.

A set of 32 basic features is used to characterize a word. These features are of two types: 5 broad-class features and 27 phonetic-event features. The five class features are: 1) Vowel/vowel-like (V/VL); 2) Long-pause (LP); 3) Short-pause (SP); 4) Unvoiced noise-like consonant (UVNLC); 5) Burst. The 27 phonetic event features represent measurements corresponding to phoneme-like occurrances.

During training, the system automatically extracts a time-normalized feature map each time the speaker repeats a given word.

The applications for such a system are enormous: for business: banking, stock control, quality control and inspection, order entry, cartography, automated material handling, numerical control programming; for avaiation in-flight control; for the home: control of heating, air-conditioning, t.v., light, etc.

In the future, it is anticipated that such computers will be used in security systems, in telephone-response systems, and in most other forms of education, including language and translation instruction and speech-therapy.

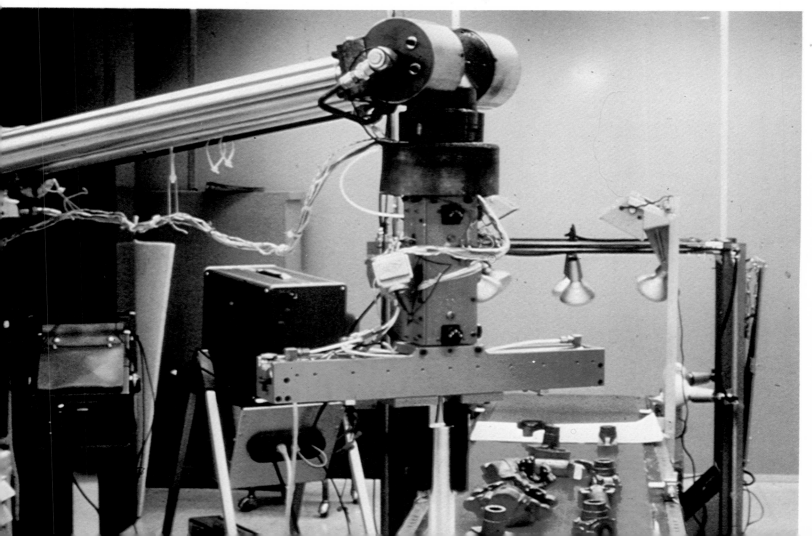

With a *voice-response computer system*, a salesman can place orders quickly and simply from any place he happens to be by using a standard telephone system, linked to a portable computer terminal. After telephone connection is established, he is linked to a central minicomputer that incorporates a voice-response unit. If too busy to hold the telephone receiver, he could place it on an acoustic coupler. As he works, the salesman records his orders on a portable terminal keyboard, while the voice-response unit confirms acceptance of the details, or points out mistakes so that they can be corrected. The voice unit, which can have a vocabulary of up to 240 words, recorded in predetermined phrases tailored to the work required, always tells the user when he may begin transmission and acknowledges completion. Each item, however, may be acknowledged by only a tone or a voice signal that merely gives the OK or else repeats some or all of the input detail. In all cases, a wide range of verification routines may be applied.

Order data, which is collected on magnetic tape by the minicomputer, is later transferred to a different computer for processing. The central minicomputer which later analyzes the data, logs the duration of the call as well, enabling the salesman to be reimbursed.

Apart from the obvious benefits of cost, time-saving, and speedier cash flow, the computer can also screen orders, rejecting invalid items such as special offers after expiry of the deadline, discontinued lines, or insufficient information.

called phonemes. The E.M.I. Threshold voice reading computer, which was first used in 1977, can recognise thirty-two of these basic sounds. By putting several phonemes together at the same time, it can learn to recognise whole words spoken by its operator. During a training session, each word has to be repeated five times. The computer then takes the average from the five examples and stores an electrical pattern of this sound in its memory. It can recognise words in any language provided they have been learned in a training session. This is because the basic phonemes are common to all languages. If the computer is taught Japanese, it will respond to Japanese instructions. And even if the operator has a speech impediment, the computer learns to recognise the individual way in which he speaks. If a person speaks with a lisp, then provided he always speaks with the same lisp the computer will understand him. Already, the Threshold machine is proving invaluable as a means of checking stock in large stores. The operator simply talks to the machine while he handles the items in question. Although it is extraordinarily difficult to increase the efficiency of such voice-reading systems because of the complexity of human speech, the task is being undertaken. Provided all goes well, it is possible that computers will

eventually equal or exceed human ability in recognising speech.

Apart from voice controlled computers, computers which reply verbally instead of having to produce information or data in the form of cards or punch tape, have been devised. This has been made possible through the development of something called a 'floppy disk', like a gramophone record, on which the necessary vocabulary is recorded. In order to reply to a request, the computer positions the play-back arm to reproduce the word required. These systems, which have been in use since the 1960s, are not designed to recognise the human voice: the computer is interrogated by pressing specially coded keys or by dialling signals on a telephone-type keyboard. However, Texas Instruments have developed a silicon chip which can generate up to 10,000 different speech sounds, making a combination system of computer voice-response and voice-control a practical possibility.

At present, the range of labour-saving gadgets and novelty devices available for the home is enormous. One example of this is the bewildering array of equipment former racing driver Sterling Moss has installed into his own home. His house in London's Mayfair district offers guests a glimpse of some of the many things which could become common-

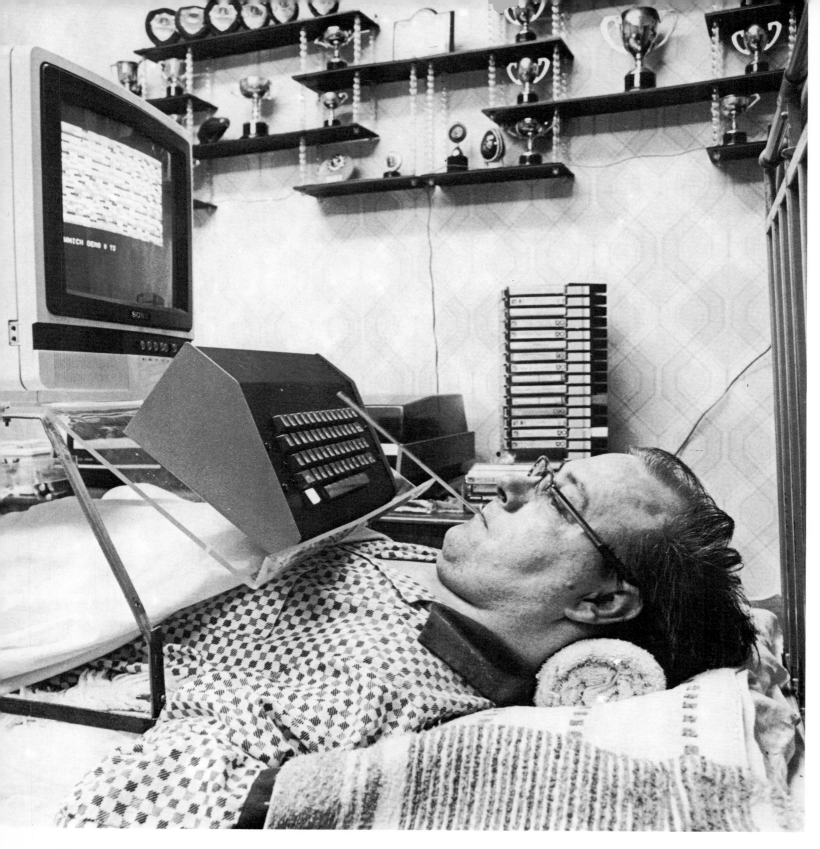

This *home computer* has opened up a new world to disabled ex-serviceman Chick Smith. For example, he can now read books stored in the computer's memory tapes without needing assistance to turn the pages. He operates the keyboard with a chopstick held in his mouth.

place in the future: he can fill the bath and regulate its temperature and depth from a set of switches in his study; keep the lavatory seat at constant body temperature; and open and close curtains electrically, turning the electric lighting on or off at the same time. The house also has an intercom system connecting all rooms; automatic control of room temperature and even the level of background music; an array of hi-fi, audio, and television equipment, complete with tape, cassette, and video recorders; and a microwave oven, a microprocessor-controlled cooker unit, and a table which can be set for meals in the kitchen above the lounge and then lowered electrically

when required. And yet, even today, this fascinating combination of technological devices has been surpassed by recent developments. In 1978, the Modular Technology Company, based near London, produced a detailed design for wiring an entire home for computer control. Instead of individual switches to activate devices by remote control, the whole process of keeping the home operating could be controlled by a small, central computer.

Basically, computer programmes consist of sets of instructions telling the computer to do first one thing, then another, and, if certain conditions are met with, to carry out a further sequence

Right
The bathroom facilities in former racing driver Sterling Moss's futuristic house in London can be controlled at the touch of a button from any room. Not only can he run the bath by remote control, but he can also control the water level and temperature. Other features are a blood-warm lavatory seat and a one-way window.

Below
Slumberland's 2002 Sleepcentre
The bed in this remote-control bedroom environment can be raised or lowered electronically and can also be rotated at a slow speed. Surrounding panels offer surround-sound stereo, television (off air, video-cassette, or Ceefax information), full telephone and intercom systems (including a CCTV system to screen and interview callers at the front door or keep an eye on other rooms in the house), dictating equipment, control of lighting and curtains, and a solarium. The master control panel can also be used to select love, wake, sleep, and peace mood programmes, all of which can be pre-set.

One of the *blowpipe freight transport system's* freight trolley capsules in the loading bay of the experimental pneumatic pipeline at Milton Keynes, England. The wheeled capsules are capable of carrying one ton of goods. In the future, such systems could replace truck and railway transport.

of instructions. Even if domestic computers are given the ability to recognise spoken instructions, tasks such as planning meals may be simplified by typing the programme into the computer. This may be done on keyboards which are shaped to fit the hands, unlike the flat keyboards of today's typewriters and teleprinters. Companies such as the P.C.D. Company in Farnborough, England, have developed 'ergonomic keyboards' for computer input terminals. The fingers and thumbs fit naturally onto the specially shaped keyboard and make it possible to type more quickly than is possible with the traditional design. With such a system, the future housewife could programme the domestic computer to prepare meals, selecting as many meals ahead as she wished, and deciding at exactly what time of the day she required each one to be ready.

The future home could have integrated cooking and food storage units at the computer's disposal. Foods could be stored in pre-arranged sequences in different freezer or refrigerator compartments, and by following its programme, the computer could select the contents of particular compartments and have them automatically delivered to the cooker by mechanical devices similar to the ones already being used in vending machines all over the world. Cooking would be a very simple task for the domestic computer. Basically, all it would have to do would be to take the required ingredients for a meal from the appropriate storage place, mix them together, and cook them for the required length of time.

Apart from the cooking, and of course the washing up, the domestic computer could also take care of the shopping. With the storage system compartmentalised, the computer could be instructed each week to take stock of the contents and produce a list of any goods required for the meals to be prepared the following week. The domestic computer would produce the necessary shopping list (which could include such details as instructing that a particular commodity should be purchased only if the price is below a certain figure), and communicate by telephone with the computer in the local supermarket which may be little more than a warehouse under computer control, with no facilities for customers to visit the premises. The store's computer would then select the items required, and arrange for them to be delivered to the home. Food would be bought in special packs ready for placing in the appropriate compartments of the food storage system. The computer would place the goods by reading magnetically coded labels on each item. Payment would be made automatically,

and cash would never be needed because the computers could have direct access to the householder's bank account. Money would exist only in the form of electronic signals stored in computer memories. Even shopping delivery would be done automatically. A system of 'blowpipes' has been installed experimentally in the English town of Milton Keynes. Small freight trolleys travel along the pipes, pushed by currents of air from fans at the ends of the pipes. The goods are literally blown along to their destinations. Quite complex air-driven delivery systems, which are easy to construct, and have already been used this century in many large stores which have installed blow-pipes to deliver money to central accounting departments. Delivery systems of the future may have automatic signalling equipment activated by labels on the goods being delivered which would ensure that all goods reached the required destination.

The trend towards 'cashless' shopping would not rule out the small store offering personal service to customers, but even in those places shoppers would simply carry a 'money card' like the one already developed by the G.E.C. company in Britain. A small plastic card, similar in appearance to an ordinary credit card, on which a certain amount of cash is recorded on a magnetic strip. The

money card user can draw sums of money from his bank account by using a special machine which 'writes' the amount onto the card's magnetic strip. To pay for goods, the 'charged up' card is inserted into another machine at the store which deducts the cost of the goods purchased, writes the new balance onto the magnetic strip, and prints out a bill detailing the amount of money spent and the amount the money card is worth after the purchase. Such developments could eventually remove the need for bank notes and coins altogether.

The domestic computer could also be very helpful when it comes to keeping the children occupied. It could be programmed with countless games and educational sequences, and, when linked to the advanced telecommunications systems, the possibilities are endless. Children could call up an educational computer and receive spoken and visual information on a television set, or they could play games with friends contacted by picturephone. If equipped with voice reading abilities, computers could even conduct conversations and conduct classes. Even if computers are not sufficiently good at being able to understand the human voice, interaction with computers equipped with keyboard and television displays should increase enormously. Many of the tedious tasks of

The Bell Labs Electronic Blackboard can transmit handwriting over ordinary telephone lines for instant display on a TV monitor at distant locations. If combined with a portable conference telephone to provide accompanying audio communications, and a standard stereo tape recorder to record voice and graphics simultaneously for synchronous playback on cassette or reel-to-reel tape, people in remote areas could receive the same education as those in better funded, better staffed, and more populated areas.

19

The revolution in communications and electronics will have an increasing effect on how and where we live, with many aspects of business life becoming extensions of the domestic environment. Our urban centres and transportation systems are already experiencing difficulties in handling the massive population movements necessitated by our present commercial structure, and the need for greater efficiency in energy consumption, together with current advances in communications technology, is likely to encourage the process of decentralisation.

The illustration shows what a home of the future could look like with an area set aside for the working day. Domestic computers, already a reality, would be linked to the employers' central data banks and video coupled telephones could provide contact with several parties simultaneously enabling daily business to be conducted. It is already possible to transmit and receive printed material and the foreground shows such a unit with its ergonomically designed keyboard.

The yellow console on the left is the control point for various domestic systems such as lighting, temperature regulation, data retrieval and home entertainments, for example the giant wall mounted television screen of the kind currently under development.

education could be taken out of the human teacher's hands, leaving him to concentrate on the jobs that require his particular skills, and a great deal of education could be done at home. Pupils would go to school not primarily for learning, but for social reasons and for gaining personal experience with a human teacher. In essence, these children of the future would be using a system not very different from the conference television systems already available to businessmen in some countries. With the advances taking place in telephone communications, it will be possible one day for people to deal with each other on a day to day basis over visual telephone systems hundreds of thousands of miles apart. Such developments could almost eliminate the need to travel. The future employee could work from home using sophisticated communications links with office, factory or other place of work; and the advance of automation in business and industry through the large scale use of micro-electronic devices, combined with the new communications systems should accelerate this trend. People could then live wherever they chose — and not necessarily close to a town or other centre of work. It would also be possible to work in one country while living in another, the work being done remotely by means of telecommunications. Because of this, countries with an excess of job vacancies could employ

workers in places with high unemployment without having to apply for immigration permits.

Even if separate office buildings remain part of our social and physical environment, they could change drastically, and the output in terms of productive work performed could improve greatly as well. To the regret of many people, the traditional secretary may become virtually obsolete. In modern offices, typewriters are already being replaced by word processing machines — typewriter keyboards which 'write' characters onto a television display screen. Letter writing can thus be made a great deal simpler because errors can be corrected electronically without erasing or retyping the entire page. Word processing machines can also facilitate the writing of business letters, many of which use a few key phrases over and over again. These phrases can be stored in an electronic memory and printed out at the touch of a single button. Then, when the letter has been completed on the screen, it can be printed out rapidly in perfect form. The word processing machines can also be used to feed information directly into a computer memory for instant transfer to another word processing machine or computer display terminal in another office, saving the time taken by sending letters through the post. The word processors can also be equipped with microprocessor 'brains'

which enable them to perform tedious tasks such as counting the total number of products sold in a whole series of transactions, or performing statistical analysis of the relative success of different marketing techniques. Using electronic word processing systems linked to computers, executives of the future will be able to spot problems rapidly and obtain computer analyses from which they can develop a plan of action for future guidance. The task of filing documents and letters could also be done with the minimum of human effort since files could be kept in a computer memory, ready for instant recall whenever needed.

A glimpse into the future of another vital area of business — stock-broking — can be seen at the Cincinnati Stock Exchange, located in the Ukranian Building in Jersey City, New Jersey, where the world's first, fully automatic electronic stock exchange has been constructed. In many ways, it typifies the twin developments of communications and computers. Customers and dealers in Cincinnati make transactions in the usual way, but everything is carried out within the computers of the electronic exchange situated hundreds of miles away in New Jersey. By using computer power, buyers and sellers can be matched to give the best prices for all concerned, and transactions can be expedited. In a future situation, when all stock exchanges may

be automatic, a uniformity of buying and selling could be established throughout a country or indeed throughout the world. By ensuring that every customer gets the best possible price wherever he may be, electronic stock exchanges could go a long way towards stabilising stock markets. Extended to commodities and currency deals, in the future countries may avoid some of the artificial economic penalties of unexpected price fluctuations and panic buying at an international level.

Among the many other industrial processes which are already being automated by means of microprocessors, welding is a good example of one which could be universally useful. The British Oxygen Company has developed a robot welder with a microprocessor brain. To learn a welding job, it has to be operated once by a skilled welder on a sample of the work to be repeated, during which time each movement is recorded in the microprocessor's memory. Once the robot welder has learned how to do the job in question, it can be left to carry on alone, repeating the job indefinitely.

Fully automated factories are already being designed using computer and microprocessor control. At the Warren Spring Laboratory in Stevenage, near London, an engineering team has designed a system which should make it possible for a single operator to run an entire factory. The great step forward which makes this possible is the method by which different machines involved in a manufacturing process, for example, can 'talk' to each other and pass on information about the state of the product being manufactured and about any problems which have emerged. This has been achieved by adopting a system called packet switching which is already being widely used in data communications over telephone lines. A 'packet' of information, a sequence of coded messages, is transmitted from the central control computer to the machine which needs to be controlled. At the beginning of the data sequence is an 'address' code that ensures that only the specifically selected machine receives the particular packet of instructions. This has made it possible to arrange all of the machines involved in a factory process in a loop,

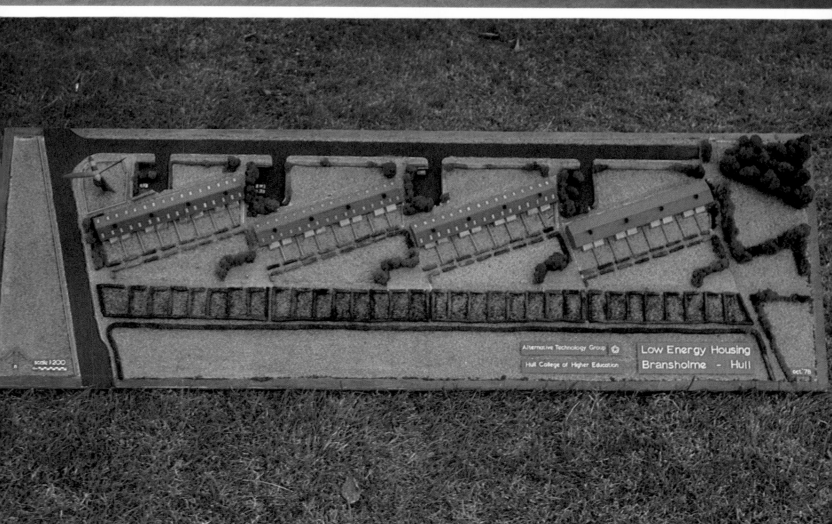

Opposite top
The *Apple II Personal Computer* can help designers and engineers visualize every part of a building or machine they are designing, keep track of every stage in the design process, spot faults, and make suggestions about improving layout.

Opposite bottom
The new *low energy housing estate* designed by the Hull School of Architecture requires only a small fraction of the energy used by ordinary houses. This is achieved by using a communal windmill, high insulation standards, heat recovery systems from waste water, and other technical innovations aimed at reducing energy consumption and waste.

Below
The *autonomous house* carries many of the systems used in the autartic house: insulating shutters (1), air to air heat recovery unit (2), alternator (3), solar panels (4), vertical axis wind turbine (5), W.C. flush tank (6), drinking water tank (7), nitrogen collection store (8), services area (9), services duct (10), sewage digester (11), pre-heat tank (12), rock or earth heat storage bed (13), solar collector pump (14), workshop (15).

linked by a single optical fibre cable. Because of the loop arrangement, the packets of instructions can travel by two different routes to any machine. Thus, if the loop is broken for maintenance or any other reason, all machines remain operative. Each individual machine also has a microprocessor that interprets the incoming signals and activates the machine according to the instructions, making it possible for a wide range of different machines, made at different times and in different places, to understand the same coded messages from the central computer. With such a system, the need to install new plant would be reduced, quality control would be performed under the watchful eye of a computer, and the industrial plant would be operational twenty-four hours every day.

Computers are also increasingly helpful in professional fields such as design engineering where they can help design complicated three dimensional structures. Whereas a human engineer may find it difficult or impossible to visualise every part of a complicated design, the computer can accurately keep track of every stage in the design process, spot faults, and make helpful suggestions about improving layout. Presented with the requirements for a final blueprint, the computer can help the designer

produce a large number of possible blueprints satisfying the basic criteria, any one of which may ultimately be chosen for the job. When the final choice is made, the computer can communicate directly with other computers which then automatically control robot production equipment to build the desired product. When computer-aided systems become widely used, it should be possible to produce even quite specialised gadgets very cheaply. The result will be that any task capable of being mechanised, could be done, or any item needed to be produced in however limited numbers, could be made available quickly and cheaply.

In the design of future homes and offices, paramount importance is likely to be given to the conservation of energy and resources, and to the reduction of pollution. In the past, many buildings were designed by architects mainly concerned with the visual characteristics of their creation, resulting in heat being released to the outside as fast as heating units could supply it. At present, large cities are hotter than the surrounding countryside. London, for example, has its own 'micro-climate' which is usually three degrees hotter than the surrounding country. Simple steps, such as installing good insulation, would

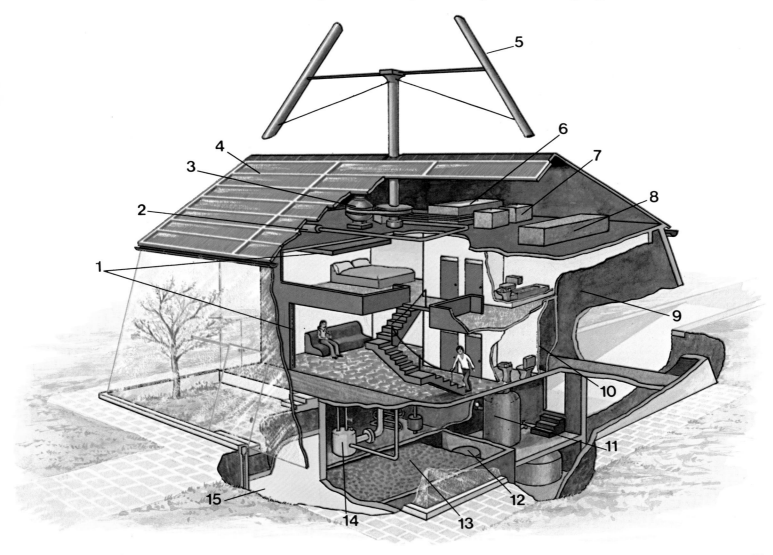

undoubtedly reduce heat wastage and reduce fuel bills. In the future, more and more architects will combine their skills with those of engineers who will advise how best to incorporate energy-saving constructions to take maximum advantage of such factors as solar heating. The engineers will also be concerned with the electrical and mechanical installations which are controlled by the domestic computer. Altogether, these new homes are likely to be designed for technical performance as much as for visual appeal.

Individual houses, or more likely housing estates, may be almost self-sufficient in energy. The Hull School of Architecture in England recently designed a housing estate consisting of thirty-two houses with high standards of insulation, shutters over the windows, heat recovery systems to extract heat from waste water, and a communal windmill, 25 metres tall, with rotors 20 metres in diameter, which supplies three-quarters of the electrical energy needed by the estate. The remaining energy is obtained from small, solid fuel burners.

The ultimate home of the future, which may become very popular especially in isolated rural areas, is the so-called autonomous house, a house which is completely independent of outside sources of energy, and makes use of natural, renewable energy sources such as sunlight, windpower, and heat from the ground. It has to be built to the highest standards of insulation and with the ability to recycle waste heat, water, and waste materials. As the name implies, the autonomous house can support its occupants under all conditions almost irrespective of what is happening in the world outside. As such, these houses may appeal to people who wish to get away from urban areas and maintain a diversity of life-styles in spite of the increasing uniformity of facilities in the technological world of the future. If present-day civilisation is ever torn apart by war, the occupants of such homes may be the citizens who will be in a position to build up their countries once again.

One of the leading designs for an autonomous house comes from the Department of Architecture at Cambridge University in England, which in the 1970s had become something of a Mecca for the so-called alternative technologies – approaches to engineering and building which take the maximum advantage of natural sources of energy and which can be constructed simply and without elaborate machinery or equipment. In the Cambridge autonomous house, waste water is re-cycled by being filtered through sand and other mineral filters. Final cleaning is done

Opposite

Dr Adnan Tarcici, a Yemeni diplomat, serves his daughter Zina with sausages and hamburgers cooked on *Sunny Side Up*, the solar cooker which he invented and patented. Quick, easy, and clean, this cooker can be folded-up into a neat package ready to be carried on a picnic wherever the sun is shining.

Above

This model *autartic house*, designed by Alexander Pike, who is Director of the Department of Architecture at Cambridge University is designed to be self-sufficient in power — although not in food — and is to be built as a mass-produced autonomous housing system for remote, marginal areas. The aerogenerator on the roof provides wind power sufficient for all domestic appliances.

by algae which grow on the bacteria, consume it, and then become a source of animal or even human food. The sewage and kitchen wastes go into a septic tank where they are converted by bacteria into a harmless residue suitable for use as fertiliser (a process already operative in large scale sewage works). The house has a plot of land for growing vegetables and for rearing a few animals, making it almost self sufficient in food. As well as re-cycled water, the inhabitants also use rainwater that is collected in a pond on the roof, and is distilled by solar heat under the pond's glass roof.

Most of the rooms, which are designed to face south, have windows inclined at about fifteen degrees to the vertical so that in winter the Sun shines directly into them, giving the maximum warmth. At night, these windows can be covered by shutters under automatic control to keep the warmth inside. The shutters are made from hollow tanks that can hold water to absorb solar heat and provide hot water. A windmill on the roof generates electric power, and a further process of sewage digestion by bacterial action produces methane gas used for cooking. There is an

earth wall on one side of the house which, apart from being cheap to build, absorbs heat during the day-time and releases it at night to keep the house warm. The house also has a heat pump, a device which works like a refrigerator in reverse, extracting heat from the ground when there is not enough solar heat. The heat pump can also be reversed in hot weather to cool the house. By 1978, detailed plans for the house were fully drawn up, and the prospect is that a family or community will soon live in it as an experimental venture.

The Communications Explosion

The ability to communicate through speech and writing has given humans pre-eminence over the other animals on Earth, and the invention of the telegraph, telephone, radio, and television has increased this difference even further and has advanced the level of our civilisation. Before the end of the century, we are likely to experience yet another quantum leap in communications efficiency and techniques which may fundamentally alter our life-styles. Indeed, a bewildering variety of vastly improved electronic methods of communication have already been developed and are awaiting commercial application.

One typical candidate for radical change during the coming communications revolution is the newspaper. There are currently so many sources and causes of delay between the time the news is reported and the time it is printed that present-day newspapers are normally out of date by the time we buy them. Individual copies have to travel sometimes hundreds of kilometers from the printing press to news-stands and door-steps – an outdated system in an age when electronic systems are capable of flashing out information to any destination at the speed of light.

Modern communications are already being used to an increasing extent in the newspaper industry. Journalists can now write their stories directly onto a 'visual display unit', which looks like a television screen with a typewriter keyboard attached to it. This is usually part of what is now called a 'word processing system'. The journalist and his editor can make adjustments to the text and leave the machine to fit the finished article into the desired format automatically. Then, at the touch of a button, the story is sent into a computer which fits it onto the page lay-out, ready for printing. Another current method of cutting down production and distribution time is to reproduce a master copy of the newspaper in different cities simultaneously by means of facsimile machines connected over telephone lines. The paper can then be printed as close as possible to the readers who will eventually receive the copies. But with this system, the final

stage of transporting the finished product to shops, and ultimately to the reader, still remains time consuming.

The solution to all of these problems is the fully electronic newspaper. A system generally known as 'viewdata', by which news is transmitted over telephone lines, makes it possible to reproduce a newspaper on the screen of a specially adapted television set. An alternative system called 'teletext', enables viewers to select the category of news desired. The information is transmitted by means of data signals encoded with a television broadcast carrying an ordinary programme. An ordinary television receiver does not register the teletext signal, but a receiver equipped with decoding gear can reproduce the pages selected by the viewer. The same journalists who are currently writing for conventional newspapers and magazines are contracted to write for viewdata and teletext systems. In the case of 'viewdata', which at present offers a much larger number of pages than 'teletext', the subscriber can automatically be charged for the use of any particular page, but free pages, such as those including advertisements, exist as well. As with ordinary newspapers, charges to the subscriber can be channeled to the organisation producing the papers or even to the journalist compiling the page. The future reader of such electronic newspapers would probably be able to use the same television receiver for both the 'teletext' and 'viewdata' systems. Due to the falling prices of electronic communications, something which is expected to continue for several decades, these systems will probably become the cheapest means of obtaining visually presented information. By adding a teleprinter or a facsimile reproduction unit to the electronic newspaper, the reader would also be able to print out any page of information required for long term use. The entire technology is already proven, and the advantages of speed and the saving in distribution costs and paper should rapidly establish the electronic newspaper for general public use. Indeed, the world's first commercial viewdata system, called 'Prestel', was inaugurated in

1979 in London by the British Post Office.

The widespread use of viewdata television receivers wired into telephone circuits could promote the development of another novel form of communication – the visual telephone. The Bell Telephone Company has already tested visual telephones commercially under the trade name Picturephone. There may never be sufficient demand for visual telephones to make it economically feasible to install television sets exclusively for this purpose, but a very small modification to the viewdata receiver, and the addition of a miniature television camera, could make the visual telephone system more accessible. This system may prove to be of the greatest benefit to the business community, who may use visual telephones to transmit diagrams and to display objects under discussion. As with viewdata, it would also be possible to make facsimile reproductions of visual telephone pictures.

It would be fairly logical for the businessman or professional person of the future to be equipped with a communications console that combines the full range of electronic communications systems. The visual telephone, which would be at the peak of this hierarchy of equipment, would probably be the most costly, and would only be used when the subject matter merited it. There would also be a video recorder to record moving pictures from the visual telephone screen in addition to teletext and viewdata facilities linked to teleprinter and facsimile units for keeping permanent records of the electronic output. A typewriter keyboard would also be available for sending written information over telephone lines as well as for use as a computer terminal. The console may be equipped with special facilities such as a small computer capable of dealing with incoming calls. Last but not least would be the ordinary telephone which the future businessman may use as much as, or even more than, he does today. These various communications methods would be charged to the customer at different rates. The telephone would perhaps remain one of the cheapest systems, but because technical developments promise to promote the present trend of falling costs, all electronic communications systems are likely to become intrinsically cheap.

At present, most telephones are connected by a two-wire, low-capacity system which is capable of coping adequately with speech channels only. Since viewdata systems are designed to require no extra capacity than this, they can be connected to existing telephone lines. Both the visual telephone and its cousin, conference television, require

high-capacity telephone lines in order to reproduce an adequate picture. Indeed, a television picture requires between five hundred and one thousand times as much telephone line capacity as the ordinary speech channel. Therefore, before visual telephones can be installed on a large scale, the capacity of telephone transmission links has to be increased, perhaps by replacing existing lines with co-axial cables.

One alternative would be to use optical fibres: tiny strands of highly pure glass which carry laser light. In just the same way as messages can be modulated on to a radio 'carrier wave', laser light waves can be modulated to carry telephone calls. They can carry vastly greater numbers of simultaneous signals compared with radio waves or even microwaves. In contrast to standard transmission wires – which incorporate copper, an expensive metal – optical fibres are made from one of the most abundant elements on earth – silicon. Because copper reserves are becoming depleted rapidly, it will one day become economical to remove all existing copper connections and replace them with optical fibres, and it is quite possible that the value of the reclaimed copper could cover the costs of the entire conversion.

It is a happy coincidence that optical fibres should be not only the potentially cheapest telephone transmission system, but also have the highest capacity easily enough for visual telephone use. In the future, optical fibre telephone lines are likely to be used for transmitting digital

Above
This *portable computer terminal*, Data Dynamics Tele-zip, can be connected to a central computer via the public telephone system.

Opposite
This *portable telephone* – the 'Carry Phone' – is a boon for those continually on the move. Weighing 4½ kgs (10 lbs) it can be used vitually anywhere.

signals, a modern-day equivalent of the Morse Code, and an ideal medium for reducing telephone interference and 'line noise'. Present-day telephone systems operate by means of what is called analogue transmission. This is a method whereby sound is encoded onto carrier waves which fluctuate either in size (amplitude modulation: AM) or frequency (frequency modulation: FM) and is then reconverted into audible signals at the receiving end. In the case of digital transmission, however, the sound is coded as a stream of pulses like Morse Code. The advantage of digital signals is that interfering noise doesn't normally affect the pulses: either a digital pulse is lost altogether, which does not happen in an adequately designed telephone system, or it gets through to the other end of the line. Provided a digital pulse reaches the remote end, the original sound can be reconstructed with little if any degradation of the signal. Another advantage of digital signals is that they lend themselves ideally to being switched and routed by electronic means. Most telephone exchanges throughout the world still use electro-mechanical switches to connect and route telephone calls. These devices, which move physically to make or break contact as a result of signals transmitted by dialling a telephone number, have proved reliable throughout the twentieth

century, but they have a tendency to wear out. In contrast, the transistor, which has no moving parts, and which can basically be used as an electronic switch, does not wear out, and never needs replacing. The advantages of electronic switching, which is suitable for digital but not analogue signals, have been even more obvious since the development of electronic circuits in which thousands of transistor circuits are mass-produced and incorporated into a small slice of silicon. Such silicon 'chips', as they have come to be known, make it possible to replace bulky telephone exchanges with electronic devices no bigger than a matchbox. The only limitation to the miniaturisation possible is due to the size of transmission wires and power lines leading into the devices. Electronic systems perform much the same basic task as electro-mechanical systems, but because they are cheap, reliable, compact, and can be wired together in very large numbers, they can perform complex and large-scale tasks which electro-mechanical systems could never do economically. Another advantage is that, because of their digital signal capability, they can easily be connected up to computers, which are also operated by digital signals. With such a system, complicated manoeuvres such as holding an incoming call while the subscriber

makes another call on the same telephone, and re-routing calls onto another number automatically, become routine. In principle, any task which can be done by a computer can be done by electronic telephone systems linked to computers. Although present-day analogue telephone signals are already being used for communication between computers, the signals have to be converted into digital form at each end of the line. With fully electronic telephone systems, the conversion equipment will not be needed, and most telephone users will ultimately have access to the wide range of tasks which computers can perform.

Within a present-day conurbation such as Los Angeles, London, or Paris, almost every business is utterly dependant on the telephone. Brave efforts are often made to re-locate businesses away from such megalopoli, but two factors hinder the success of such schemes: the cost of making long distance telephone calls, and the cost of travelling to meet businessmen in other areas. However, through the use of communications satellites, which can connect the whole world by means of high-quality telephone links, it should ultimately be possible to have all telephone calls charged at a fixed rate, or indeed to charge a simple rental for using a telephone service, irrespective of the num-

Left
This *fibre guide cable* contains twelve ribbons of light guides, each encapsulating twelve glass fibres and is protected by a sheath embedded with steel wires. A similar cable with twenty-four light guides was used to carry voice, television, and data signals in the Chicago Lightwave project.

Opposite top
Light transmitted through *optical fibres* (made of glass) offers a potentially greater capacity for telecommunications than conventional cables. The glass fibres shown are only a few thousandths of an inch in diameter each.

Opposite bottom
Before being launched, satellites are tested in special chambers which simulate the environment of space. Here, the *Orbital Test Satellite* (OTS) is being tested in an anechoic chamber — so named because its walls reflect no electromagnetic (i.e. light, radio waves, etc) radiation, and thus simulate the darkness of space.

Below
Orbital Test Satellites have to undergo vigorous pre-launch testing to guarantee manoeuvrability in space.

INTELSAT V is one of a network of communications satellites permanently in orbit around the Earth. They provide long-distance relay of telephone, data, and television signals. Such satellites can bring international linkage to small, isolated countries which have no prospect of joining an efficient international telephone network by any other means. The International Telecommunications Satellite Organisation (INTELSAT) is responsible for co-ordinating global satellite communications.

ber of calls made, no matter where those calls are routed. The impact of being able to dial international telephone calls, not to mention trunk calls within any individual country, at no more than local charge rates could be immense. This truly world-wide link up of information services, co-ordinated by huge computers, would obviate the need for travel and would permanently change the face of world business, commerce and industry.

Like the very first artificial satellites, the Sputniks, the early experimental communications satellites, such as the 'Telstar' of the early 1960s, flew a few

hundred miles above the Earth's surface and completed their orbit in less than two hours. Transmitting and receiving ground stations could view them for only short periods of time, but nevertheless the satellites produced spectacular results and made trans-Atlantic television transmissions possible. Continuous relay 'geostationary' satellites, satellites which remain at fixed points relative to the Earth's surface, were then developed to act as continuous relay stations in the sky. Their apparently miraculous feat of hovering continually above the same point on the ground was achieved by using higher orbital altitudes. A satellite

boosted out to a height of nearly 36,000 kilometers flys around the Earth only once every twenty-four hours. Provided its orbit is aligned with the equator, it is possible for such a satellite to circle the Earth at exactly the same rate as the Earth rotates on its axis, thereby maintaining a relative stationary position. Ground stations, with their large dish-shaped directional radio aerials, can then be pointed permanently at the geostationary satellite to achieve continuous radio communication between various parts of the world via the satellite relay stations. By the mid 1970s, the Intelsat organisation was operating eight geo-

stationary satellites. With 165 ground stations in many different countries, in many parts of the world it soon became easier to make an international call than to obtain a local number. At the same time, world-wide live television coverage of big sporting events such as the Olympic Games was made possible. It is predicted that by the year 2000 several hundred geostationary satellites will be in orbit. Many of these could be large multiple assemblies which could carry huge arrays of transmission and reception aerials. They would be ferried up into orbit in kit form by the Space Shuttle (the re-usable space craft being

This American *radio telescope base* is designed specifically as a relay station for the network of communications satellites which are in continual orbit around the earth.

35

Hundreds of artificial satellites now silently orbit our planet and although the majority of these are specialized research units, others directly contribute to our daily lives in such areas as meteorology, surface nagivation and communication.

The key communication satellites are in geostationary orbit, maintaining a fixed position in relation to the Earth's surface and providing communcation links over the entire globe, while the greater number lie much closer in deteriorating orbits.

Launch costs are very high and the satellites themselves are subject to damage or maulfunction within their five to ten year lifespan, but the development of re-usable spacecraft, such as the Rockwell Shuttle, make servicing and repair a practical possibility.

developed by the United States), and would be constructed in space.

The all-purpose communications satellite of the future would undoubtedly carry its own computer, and, as with present-day satellites, would generate all its power requirements from solar cells. The information-carrying capacity of such immense space structures would make today's communications satellites seem like a child's toys. In addition to the high radio frequencies already being used to beam signals around the world, satellites could also exploit the still higher frequencies of the electromagnetic spectrum, stretching into the infra-red range. Up until now, it has not been possible to use such frequencies for reliable communication because they are absorbed easily by water vapour and dust in the atmosphere, but with a large number of geostationary satellites in orbit, it will be possible to provide sufficient alternative paths through the atmosphere to route any telephone message around interfering clouds. Furthermore, when signals can be carried by laser beams shining up to the satellites and back down to the ground stations in place of radio waves, the signal-carrying capacity will be increased again by a large factor.

At present, a very limited choice of television and radio programmes is available compared to what is technically possible. By the year 2000, it should be possible to make almost all programmes being broadcast in whatever country available to almost every listener or viewer in any country. Even the poorer countries are likely to benefit because it will be possible to beam television programmes directly down to small isolated villages by satellite. The villages would have large communal aerials which would either feed individual television sets or be used to produce a large picture for communal viewing in the style of a cinema. Communicating directly with satellites is also likely to become more common as the 21st century approaches because television crews, who travel to different parts of the world to cover news and sporting events, will be able to take with them a portable satellite ground station such as the one developed by Britain's Independent Broadcasting Authority. Once the station has been transported to the news scene, the crew can feed the pictures from their cameras directly to the portable ground station's transmitter. This has a dish type aerial, rather like a radar dish, pointing towards the goestationary satellite. A clear signal can then be received at television headquarters almost anywhere in the world.

Apart from satellites, new technology on the ground will also improve reception and expand the range of available television programmes. When optical fibre transmission lines are fitted to every telephone, a large number of television programmes could also be sent by telephone cable. This means that the electrical signal produced by the microphone and camera is carried by a light wave. The electrical signal is then reproduced in electrical form in the television or radio receiver and converted back into a television or radio programme. As with ordinary telephone signals, it is now possible to encode the electrical signals digitally, forming a sequence of pulses. A digital receiving set can then decode the pulses, reducing the interference and

Above

The Jodrell Bank Mark I, the first of the giant, dish-shaped radio telescopes, was designed to receive radio noise from space — radiations produced by hot atoms in the celestial bodies.

Opposite

The European Space Agency's (ESA) *MAROTS B satellite*, a maritime version of the European Communications Satellite (ECS) will provide direct telephone and telex links between ships in distant oceans and shore stations in the U.K. and elsewhere, giving a much needed improvement in quality and capacity over existing facilities.

giving a higher quality reproduction of picture and/or sound. Indeed there will be a strong incentive to convert all broadcast and telecommunications signals into digital form as they can be easily processed by computers. And since computers, and their small cousins the microprocessors, are likely to be ubiquitously involved with business and industry and most other aspects of life in the not-too-distant future, it will be eminently sensible to convert most information-carrying media to digital form.

By the year 2000, telecommunications will still be in its infancy, but it will have developed enough to make possible vigorous efforts at contacting other intelligent beings on other planets elsewhere in the Galaxy, if there are such civilisations. They may have overlooked our planet up until now, but the moment we start broadcasting into space with high quality, powerful radio signals, such remote civilisations will have the opportunity to notice us perhaps for the first time. With this realisation in mind, it is possible that renewed efforts will be

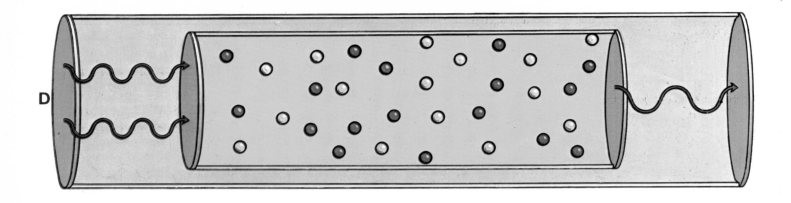

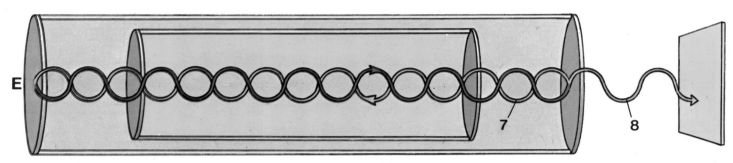

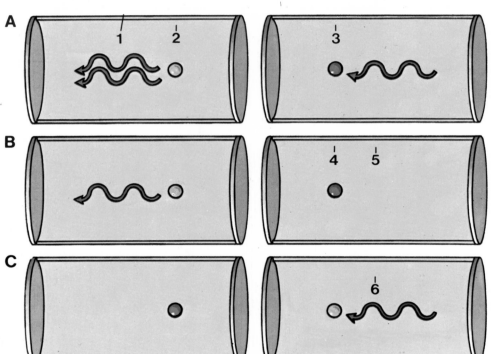

A

1 2 3

B

4 5

C

6

In communications systems of the future, radio waves will be replaced by *lasers*. These will greatly increase signal-carrying capacity. The diagram shows how the laser reproduces its beam of intense, pure light.

Left

A. A photon (1) (unit of energy) is fired at an atom (2) which becomes excited (3).

B. The excited atom can return to an unexcited state (4) by releasing its energy as a photon of light (5). This is known as spontaneous emission.

C. An excited atom can be induced to emit its stored photon of light. By firing a photon at an already excited atom, the atom can be induced to return to an unexcited state by emitting two photons of light (6). This is known as stimulated emission.

D. The atoms here are raised from the unexcited state to the excited state, spontaneous emission will occur until more than half the atoms are excited. At this point stimulated emission starts to occur as photons are more likely to hit an excited atom than an unexcited one.

E. This activity takes place in a tube with reflective ends. As the light energy is bounced back and forth it falls into a regular wave pattern (7). By making one end of the tube a partially reflecting surface, some of this 'coherent' light (8), the laser beam, can be emitted whilst the rest is returned through the medium.

Opposite top

Artist's impression of *Project Cyclops*, an interstellar search system, showing an array of 100 metre (320 ft) radio telescopes.

Opposite bottom

Arthur C. Clarke has been involved in a project mounted by the Indian government, in collaboration with N.A.S.A., to install receiving antennae in many isolated villages throughout India so that good quality television reception can be provided at a fraction of the cost of building conventional transmitters.

made to transmit meaningful broadcasts into space for the benefit of other creatures on other planets by using huge dish-shaped radial aerials like the ones which are currently used for radio astronomy. On the receiving end, the advent of powerful radio telescopes makes it possible to detect radio noise from stars and galaxies in deep space, as well as intelligent signals from other civilisations if they exist. Indeed, in 1967, just such a signal was thought, briefly, to have been detected. A new type of star, later named 'pulsar' (or 'pulsating radio source') was discovered. It produced regularly-timed pulses of radio energy like a space light-house, and was thought possibly to be some sort of

galactic radio beacon erected in space for long distance space navigation purposes. Eventually, this explanation was ruled out, but astronomers are nevertheless alert to the possibility that one day they may receive truly artificial signals from space. Although deliberate efforts have already been made to search for intelligent signals, radio astronomers have been aware that in all the universe the chances of locating the particular planet which has taken the trouble to beam radio messages in our direction at this particular time in history are remote. But as time goes by the question will more frequently be asked: Are we alone in the Universe? Radio communications may well provide the answer.

The Energy Game

A global crisis is expected to take place around the beginning of the twenty-first century. The world is running out of oil, coal and natural gas. Nobody can be sure of precisely when supplies of these fossil fuels will be exhausted, but experts agree that the day cannot be far away when we shall be forced to use alternative sources of energy or drastically reduce the standards of living we have become accustomed to in the energy-rich twentieth century.

The future world is likely to be every bit as dependent upon energy as we are today, if not more so. Electricity, fuel for heating and cooling, and power sources for transportation, have all become essential to modern life. The modern city is particularly sensitive to interruptions of the energy supply. This was vividly illustrated during the 1977 power failure in New York. In a matter of minutes, normal life was transformed into a state of emergency when the city was plunged into sudden darkness. Traffic lights stopped working in the streets, and public-spirited citizens manned the crossroads and junctions with flashlights to guide the growing volume of motor traffic that rapidly became the only means of transportation for millions of New Yorkers. The subway trains halted in stations for lack of signalling, despite their independent power supply which unfortunately fed only the electric motors of the trains. Buses could not re-fuel because electrical filling pumps were inoperative. It was one of the hottest days of the year, and air conditioning systems no longer worked, making life intolerable in the most modern blocks which had been designed, often with no opening windows, for continuous air conditioning and central heating. Lifts and escalators were out of action forcing all citizens to climb stair-wells in darkness, holding candles for twenty, thirty or even more floors until they reached their apartments. On reaching home, citizens found refrigerators dripping water onto the floor, and the refrigerator's contents rapidly warming. If people didn't take a shower or use the toilet soon after the black-out, they later found that water supplies had run dry because electrically operated pumps, which normally keep the roof-tanks of apartment blocks full, had stopped working. Listening to the news on transistor radios, they heard a continuous running commentary about practically nothing. Most of the communications equipment supplying the studios with news had stopped working, and reporters were reduced to talking about heresay accounts and information gathered from their immediate surroundings. Meanwhile, in the city at large, the looters were out in force. In some parts of the city almost every store was raided, and store-keepers guarded their stocks with guns. Thousands of arrests took place, but the city's prisons could not cope adequately with the sudden influx of looters arrested by the police. The final economic cost of this sudden interruption of electric power has never been fully assessed, but, certainly, it runs into thousands of millions of dollars.

How can cities of the future be protected against such a catastrophic result from so simple a cause? One answer which is being vigorously pursued is to re-design every building and system to protect against possible power failure. But before this can be implemented, the most important consideration is to guarantee electricity supplies by installing reliable power stations and anticipating future electricity demand so that a nation always keeps a healthy margin of power generating capacity to cope with any unexpected failure. Nevertheless, as the traditional fuels – coal, oil and gas – become scarce, catastrophes such as the New York blackout can only be averted by transferring our reliance to other, more abundant sources of power. This is one argument for installing nuclear power stations.

The peaceful use of nuclear power is the fulfillment of a modern dream which began as a nightmare. Much of the stimulus for nuclear research was provided by the need to win a war, and when atoms of uranium were found to be capable of splitting apart and releasing energy of immense proportions, it soon became possible to make nuclear bombs.

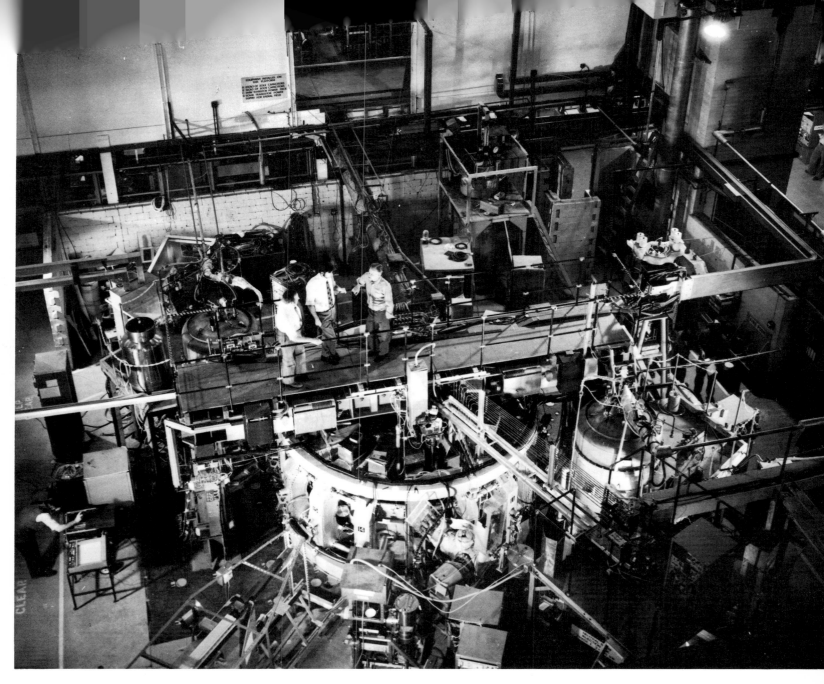

These concentrate the destructive power equivalent to many thousands of tons of conventional high explosive into a space small enough to carry in an aeroplane and, to its horror, as the bombs fell on Hiroshima and Nagasaki, the world learned what immense power had been released from the atom's inner parts. But the same process can also be harnessed in a controlled manner to provide heat, and, ultimately, electricity. However, there are environmental objections to the use of nuclear power: the one-in-a-million chance of a nuclear explosion taking place at a nuclear reactor is an ever present possibility; the mining, manipulating, and re-processing of nuclear fuels is a potential hazard to workers involved because of the risk of accidental radio-active contamination; and the disposal of highly toxic, radio-active waste materials from nuclear power stations is regarded by some as a problem which has not been solved and could threaten the health of thousands of generations if not properly dealt with.

A timely reminder of the uncharted risks of nuclear power was the accident which occurred near the town of Harrisburg, Pennsylvania, U.S.A., in 1979: a nuclear reactor went out of control and released radio-active pollutants into the atmosphere. Although leaks from nuclear power stations in other countries have occurred, the accident in Pennsylvania was by far the most serious to date, and caused governments all over the world to re-evaluate the pros and cons of providing their citizens with such a potentially hazardous but powerful source of energy.

Regarding the disposal of radio-active wastes, at present, the main hope is that it will be possible to incorporate them into a form of glass, thereby binding them in solid form, never to be released into the environment. Blocks of radio-active glass could then be lowered thousands of metres into the earth's crust, preferably in places where hard, impervious rocks such as granite exist, preventing any possible escape of the waste materials. Another ingenious idea for nuclear waste disposal, put forward by a Scottish

scientist, Dr Chris Talbot of Dundee University in Scotland, makes use of the fact that radio-active waste material continually generates heat. Dr Talbot's idea is to place containers or solid blocks of the waste into the ground of a depth where they would melt the rocks beneath them and sink continually into the Earth. This would not only dispose of the wastes, but could also be a potential source of valuable information about the inner parts of the Earth. The packages of waste materials could be tracked by scientific instruments as they descend, giving some of the first detailed information about the inner parts of our planet, effectively becoming 'inner space probes'. The major opinion within the nuclear industry appears to be that the development of such methods will ensure that the waste can be disposed of safely, without posing any hazard to future generations, but it is also argued that no policy – even the abandonment of nuclear power – can guarantee freedom from hazards in future years.

At present, some people think that

nuclear power is one of our cleanest sources of energy. According to a 1978 study conducted by the Atomic Energy Board of Canada, only natural gas seems to be cleaner and less hazardous than nuclear power. Coal and oil were found to be far more hazardous than nuclear power stations. These fuels not only produce vast quantities of sulphur dioxide gas which is absorbed by atmospheric moisture and falls as acid rain, a potential hazard to crops, but they also release more radio-activity into the environment than nuclear power stations which are (supposedly) designed to be completely contained, releasing no radio-active contamination. Fossil fuels, on the other hand, contain small quantities of radio-active impurities and these are inevitably released up the chimneys of power stations.

Apart from purely environmental dangers, the proliferation of nuclear power stations is also seen by some as a potential threat to peace because the uranium and plutonium fuels of nuclear reactors can be used to make nuclear bombs. There is a very reasonable worry that highly organised gangs of urban terrorists could obtain plutonium and, with modest laboratory facilities, make home-made bombs which could threaten the very fabric of society. Ironically, one could say that one of the great attractions of nuclear power is that uranium is not really very useful for any purpose other than generating power or building bombs – unlike the fossil fuels from which are derived countless products: chemicals, plastics, drugs, fabrics, and a whole range of modern consumer goods. Fossil fuels are vital feedstock to the chemical and manufacturing industries, and once exhausted cannot easily be replaced by any other naturally occurring raw material. With this fact in mind, it will seem almost criminal to continue burning these valuable resources if there is an alternative, cheaper means of providing electricity. This may be a crucial argument in favour of nuclear power, which is already said to be one of the cheapest methods of generating electricity.

At present, most experts within the industry are quick to point out that present-day nuclear reactors are using only a small fraction of the uranium atom's potential power. Only one part in a hundred of natural uranium consists of the isotope 235 which is used in conventional reactors. The remaining ninety-nine parts of uranium cannot be used because they consist of uranium 238 which does not split apart so easily. However, a new generation of reactors called fast breeder reactors can convert this major part of natural uranium into the element plutonium which is an ideal fuel for a modified nuclear reactor. Thus, in theory, the fast breeder reactors could provide one hundred times as much energy from the same quantity of uranium. If these reactors are used on a large scale, there is a real hope that very cheap electricity could be available for several hundred years. Also, partly because it is so potentially efficient, it is conceivable that the fast breeder reactor, which is likely to be more compact than traditional reactors, could hold greater risks of accidental nuclear explosion. The nuclear industry as a whole normally takes the view that good engineering design and planning can reduce all the potential risks of nuclear reactor operation to almost zero, but nagging doubts remain. In Britain, a recent Royal Commission on the Environment concluded that the country should not depend for energy supply on a process (the fast breeder reactor) that produces such a hazardous substance (plutonium) unless there is no reasonable alternative; and in

Two views of the *Trojan Nuclear Power plant*, built by Westinghouse, during a refuelling operation.

the United States, President Carter has made it clear that his government will leave no stone unturned in seeking reasonable alternatives to the fast breeder reactor. Keeping these and many more reservations about the use of nuclear power in mind, the future of energy generation throughout the world could take any of a number of different paths during the next century.

If the growth in world energy consumption is allowed to continue in the future, there is one source of energy which offers almost unlimited power for thousands of years to come: nuclear fusion. The process of nuclear fission, in which uranium atoms are split apart to provide energy, is basically what happens in the atomic bomb. The more powerful hydrogen bomb works by means of the nuclear process of fusion, in which hydrogen atoms are joined together (fused) by enormous heat (provided by a small atom bomb) to release yet larger amounts of energy. This is also the process by which the sun produces energy. The ultimate hope is that nuclear fusion power will be harnessed in a controlled manner, just as the atom bomb process of nuclear fission has already been harnessed in conventional nuclear reactors. Nuclear fusion has many advantages over nuclear fission. Quite apart from producing greater quantities of power, it is also a relatively clean source of energy, and it uses hydrogen as the basic fuel – an element which can be obtained in almost unlimited quantities from water. Investigations into the possibility of harnessing the nuclear fusion process in a controlled way – in effect, taming the hydrogen bomb – have been going on for more than twenty years.

In 1978, scientists at Princeton University in the United States succeeded in heating up hydrogen gas to a temperature of 60 million degrees fahrenheit and maintaining this for one tenth of a second. This was done in a hollow 'dough-nut' shaped vacuum chamber in which the hydrogen gas was suspended magnetically at the middle of the hollow tube. This technique is used in all such experimental fusion devices to avoid contact of the gas with the walls of the container. In 1981, the Princeton team plans to operate a larger vacuum chamber called the Toroidal Fusion Test Reactor which will maintain higher temperatures for still longer periods of time – long enough, it is hoped, for self-sustaining fusion reactions to take place.

In Europe, too, a fusion machine known as the Joint European Torus is being built at the Culham Laboratory in Oxfordshire, England. The Soviet Union is also well ahead with research work on experimental nuclear fusion reactors. Up until now there has been no indication as to whether fusion will ever become a practical source of energy. It is still by no means certain how the heat-energy created in a fusion reactor could be extracted and used to generate electricity, but the recent record of temperature and duration of containment set by the Princeton scientists has led to specu-

lation that the world is at last on the way to harnessing this most powerful source of energy. Many scientists working in this field of research are optimistic that practical reactors for generating electric power will be available perhaps as early as the year 2000. If they are, an era of energy abundance, which would last practically for as long as the human race survives on the planet, could begin.

However, there are limits to the allowable growth of energy consumption. One traditional penalty of increased energy consumption is increased pollution. Most air pollution is a direct result of burning coal and other fossil fuels in power stations and vehicles. Water pollution is largely the result of industrial activities, made possible by abundant energy supplies, and of sewage and other effluents produced by concentrations of human population. Noise pollution arises from our increasing ability to mechanise all manner of activities: travel, industrial production, even domestic appliances, including heating and air conditioning. But the ultimate pollutant comes from increased energy consumption of all kinds: heat pollution.

Practically all of the energy generated and used by man is converted by his activities into heat. Already, energy consumption is affecting the weather and

Above
Scale model of the *Joint European Torus (JET) vacuum chamber* which is used to heat hydrogen gas for experiments in self-sustaining fusion reactions.

Opposite top
Artist's impression of the *MOD–1 experimental wind turbine generator* currently under development by NASA at the Lewis Research Centre in Ohio. It is expected that this huge windmill will fulfill all the electricity needs of the local population.

Opposite bottom
This high speed *vertical axis or egg beater wind turbine*, here being tested by the Sandia Laboratories in Albuquerque, New Mexico, has blades with a symmetrical aerofoil section which bow out to a diameter of 420 cm (14 ft), the shape being designed to eliminate bending stresses. The electrical output is 1 kw in a 24 km (15 m) per hour wind, rising to 8 kw in a 48 km (30 m) per hour wind.

climate in many cities by warming the atmosphere. Firstly, because coal, oil, and natural gas produce carbon dioxide on burning, the atmosphere gets increasingly loaded with this gas. Some of it can be absorbed by plant life, but there are already indications that the carbon dioxide concentrations are rising as a result of the burning of fossil fuels. Climatologists point out that atmospheric carbon dioxide can produce a phenomenon called the greenhouse effect on our planet: it can trap the Sun's heat, and raise the temperature of the planet even further. Therefore, the use of fossil fuels, as well as the overall growth of energy consumption, must be limited in the future. Secondly, if the next century marks the beginning of a nuclear fusion capability, it is possible that far more heat would be generated than could safely be absorbed by the Earth and its atmosphere.

Nobody knows precisely how sensitive to disturbances such as an appreciable input of heat the atmosphere will prove to be, but the effect could be catastrophic. Conceivably, a chain of events could be unleased which would lead to the melting of the polar ice and to world-wide flooding. And this may not be the most serious effect of atmospheric heating. If the delicate balance of climate is disturbed, patterns of rainfall and sunshine may be so altered that agricultural production will be drastically affected. With the world's growing population ever more dependent on exploiting the last degree of agricultural productivity in the years ahead, populations could be decimated. The solution to this horrifying spectacle lies in making quite sure that global energy generation does not exceed the Earth's ability to radiate energy into space and dispose of it harmlessly. Up until now, the quantities of artificially generated power seem to have been too small to affect the climate in any major way, but there is an increasingly urgent body of opinion suggesting that we should transfer to the use of natural, renewable sources of energy.

By harnessing wind power, for example, man is merely taking advantage of energy provided on earth by nature. Any heat produced by this natural energy would take place whether man harnessed it or not. As with other natural energy sources, this energy is initiated by the Sun, which heats the atmosphere at different rates in different parts of the globe, depending on factors such as the nature of the earth's surface, and the number of clouds present. This huge inpouring of heat from the Sun creates strong winds as the atmosphere attempts to even out the heat distribution.

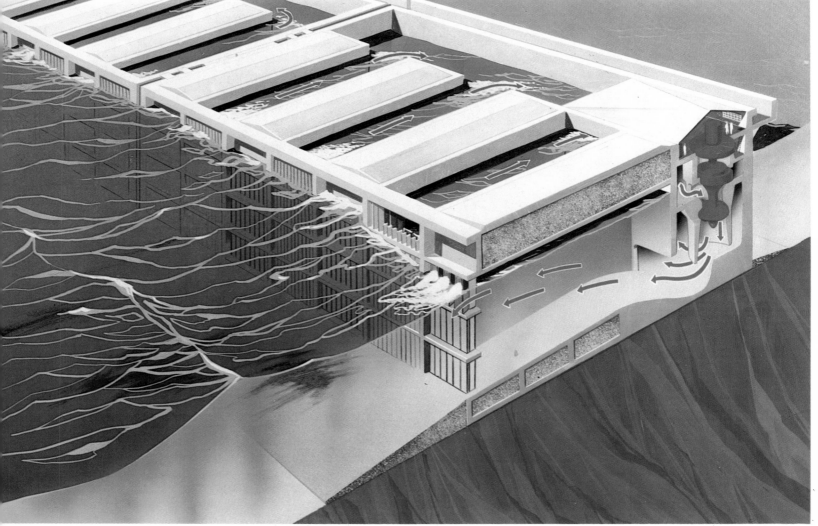

Above
Clusters of vertical-axis (1) and the more conventional horizontal axis (2) windmills anchored offshore in shallow water could provide more than 20% of U.K. electricity needs. Occupying an area of about 10 km (16 mi) square, the *windmill clusters* (approximately 400 in each) could produce about 1,000 mg of electricity and their environmental impact would be minimal. This could be linked with an *ocean thermal Power Extractor* (3) which uses the small temperature differences in the ocean to drive a heat engine. The engine is designed to operate on a temperature differential of about 4.4°C (40°F), the difference between the warm surface water and the near-freezing water far below. A 150 m (50 ft) wide fibreglass-reinforced plastic pipe would stretch from the free floating platform 12,000 m (4000 ft) down to suck up the cold water. The turbine generator would supply 100 mg of electricity.

Opposite top
Salter Ducks, here depicted by an artist, harness wave energy by rocking to and fro in the swell. The motion drives hydraulic pumps linked to electric generators.

Opposite bottom
An artist's impression of the *Russell Rectifier* which converts wave energy by using a system of small dams and hydroelectric turbines. Behind the face of the structure that is exposed to the waves there are a series of high-level reservoirs alternating horizontally with low-level reservoirs. Waves drive sea-water into the high-level reservoirs and abstract it from the low-level reservoirs. A turbine passes sea water from high-level to low-level.

Wind power has been used for hundreds of years, the classic examples being the graceful windmills of Holland. Wind-powered pumps are in very wide-spread use all over the world, as are hundreds of thousands of the American fan-type farm windmill which is also being employed to raise water. The United States also has an impressive number of small companies specialising in the manufacture of wind generators for providing electrical power in isolated places and for charging batteries that provide small amounts of electricity when the wind is not blowing. In contrast, wind generators of the future are likely to be massive installations capable of yielding sufficient electrical energy to supply whole cities.

The American government is currently financing wind power research aimed at generating enough electricity to make a significant contribution to the nation's power requirements. For example, Dr William Heronemus of the Massachusetts Institute of Technology is investigating the possibility of heating homes with wind power; and at the Sandia Laboratories in Albuquerque, New Mexico, Richard Braasch is investigating the vertical axis, or Darrieus type of windmill, which looks rather like an upside-down egg-beater standing vertically upwards, and is capable of accepting the wind from any direction. Unlike the Dutch-type horizontal axis windmill, it does not have to turn to face the wind, nor does it require a gear mounted at the top of the tower to turn the force of rotation through an angle of 90 degrees. Vertical axis windmills are cheaper and simpler to build than horizontal axis ones and thus may well solve the problem of cost which is one of the main obstacles to the further development of wind power.

Another project currently under development by the National Aeronautics and Space Administration's Lewis Research Centre in Cleveland, Ohio, is the building of two experimental wind turbine generators called MOD–1, a multi-million dollar system which truly looks ahead to the next century. These gigantic windmills are of the horizontal axis type, with rotors of more than 60 metres diameter. Each one is capable of generating up to 1.5 megawatts of electricity. This would mean that about 700 of the devices linked together could provide a similar power output to a typical modern nuclear power station of 1000 megawatts output.

In Britain, the Electrical Research Association is also anticipating the future need for wind power with designs for a large windmill which, like MOD–1, could be used in groups of hundreds or thousands as a source of power for cities of the future. In the past, the Central

Electricity Generating Board in Britain has encountered environmental objections from local residents to proposed sites for large-scale wind generators. The present, now widely accepted solution, is to site such generators at sea. Another type of British windmill which according to its inventor, Dr Peter Musgrove of Reading University, could also be sited at sea is a vertical axis windmill which features vertical vanes like the slats of a venetian blind, which rotate round the axis of the windmill. The vanes can lean outwards as the strength of the wind builds up, to spill off some of the incoming wind during gales, thereby avoiding excessive pressures on the windmill. Taking account of the widely varying wind speeds is a major problem of windmill design. Horizontal axis windmills can do this by altering the pitch of the air-screw blades. Peter Musgrove's hope is that because his vertical axis windmill can adapt more simply to changing wind speeds it will overcome the problem of cost, the principle hurdle facing wind power generators.

Although wind energy itself is a valuable renewable energy source, it also drives the ocean waves. Winds blowing for many hours gradually build up huge waves carrying large amounts of energy. The waves are in effect a concentrated, packaged, form of wind energy. Most countries with ocean shorelines could also obtain very significant quantities of energy from the waves. A maritime country such as Great Britain could supply twice her current needs of electricity by harnessing wave power around her shores. Another case in point is the coast of Somalia at the Horn of Africa. Some of the most powerful waves in the world break on the Indian Ocean shoreline of this semi-arid country. It has been proposed that not only could huge quantities of electricity be produced there, but also that the ocean waves could be used to push sea water through special filters (so-called reverse-osmosis filters) which could then yield pure water for irrigation and drinking on a scale large enough to transform the agriculture and wealth of the country. In fact, the eventual harnessing of wave power

could supply more than the world's total present-day needs, and if there is a world ban on the use of certain types of nuclear power stations, wave energy may become one of the most economical forms of natural energy. The whole future of wave energy hinges on the costs of the alternatives. Even though oil prices are now rising this valuable commodity is still being sold at what may be historically recognised as give-away prices. So because of present-day, relatively low prices of oil and uranium, wave energy looks comparatively expensive. This seems paradoxical when the energy itself is free, but large, robust engineering structures have to be built at sea to harness the energy. There are several excellent designs available already, but in no case would the cost be low. Only when the world takes a long-term view will wave energy be considered one of the better options.

One of the leading devices currently being used experimentally to harness wave energy is the so-called Salter Duck, a floating object, with a very high centre of gravity, which rocks to and fro and up

and down in the waves. The Duck was designed by Professor Salter of Edinburgh University, who took all the rules of naval architecture, normally used to develop ships which don't roll in the waves, and reversed them. In practice, hundreds of these dipping, bobbing, rolling ducks would be lined up at sea along a firm metal backbone, and the energy produced by their reaction against the backbone would be used to drive hydraulic pumps linked to electric generators. The Edinburgh University team has succeeded in getting 90% of the energy out of waves in an experimental tank using one-hundredth scale models of the ducks. Recently, one-tenth scale models have been used on Loch Ness in Scotland, a lake which has waves of about one-tenth the size of those of the Atlantic. Professor Salter expects that full-sized ducks could extract up to half of the power in ocean waves, and that after further development, it should be possible to extract nearly 100%. A full scale duck may be built soon, and provided all goes well, mass production could begin during the 1980s. Initially, the devices would be expensive to construct but could provide cheap, non-polluting, energy for the countless centuries ahead. According to the Edinburgh team, power extracted by the ducks may also be used at sea in the next century. The electricity could be used directly on sea water to make hydrogen by the process of electrolysis; to produce ammonia from water and air, providing

feedstocks for the chemical industry; or to pump off-shore oil wells, enabling extraction of more oil than is currently possible. At present about 30% of the oil in ordinary oil wells can be extracted, but with abundant wave energy, and a growing technology for releasing oil from the rocks which absorb it, a far greater percentage of underground supplies could be extracted.

Another ingenious wave-energy device is the Russell Rectifier developed by Robert Russell, director of the Hydraulics Research Centre at Wallingford in southern England. It is basically a sophisticated system combining small dams, built in shallow water, with hydro-electric turbines: tank-like structures some 300 metres long by 80 metres wide, which sit on the sea bed in depths of around 20 metres of water, and which are compartmented into high- and low-level reservoirs. Incoming waves push water into the high level reservoirs, and, by a system of valves, suck water out of the low level reservoirs, providing a continuous flow of water to drive water-turbines linked to electric generators.

Currently, several more wave-energy devices, which have been tested in model form, are being developed at the National Engineering Laboratory in East Kilbride, Scotland, and at Queen's University in Belfast, Ireland. One device consists of a system of moored, hollow buoys, one end open to the sea, which drive compressed air through turbines to generate electricity: as waves pass, air trapped within

Above
An artist's impression of a series of *hydropneumatic buoys* which are currently under investigation at the National Engineering Laboratory (NEL) in East Kilbride, Glasgow. The NEL buoy uses the same principle as the Queens University buoy. Water displacement inside the buoy causes an air current to pass through a turbine which generates electricity.

Opposite
One kind of *hydropneumatic wave power* energy device is a buoy, designed at Queens University, Belfast, with a narrow neck or orifice at the bottom, but open at the bottom. It is attached by struts to a hollow sphere, partially filled with water, so that it has zero buoyancy but considerable inertia. The whole structure, which is made of glass-reinforced-polymer, is very light.

The waterline, when at its mooring, roughly corresponds to the fattest part of the buoy. As the waves outside the buoy rise and fall, a related water movement occurs inside, forcing air up and down, like a piston in a cylinder, so that the buoy breathes in and out through the orifice at the top. A special air turbine, mounted in the orifice, is driven by the air which is forced through it. The turbine rotor is directly coupled to an electric generator mounted vertically above it.

51

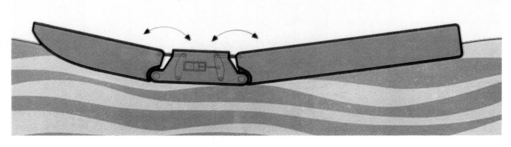

1980s, these various mechanical devices are likely to be tested, hopefully at full scale, to prepare for large-scale wave-energy harnessing by the end of the century. At present-day costs, the electricity generated would be about two or three times as expensive as electricity derived from fossil fuels or nuclear power, but the cost difference may well diminish in the future as conventional fuel prices rise.

As with all forms of energy harnessing, large-scale wave-energy power stations would affect the environment. Shipping and fishing could be disrupted to some degree, but there are also advantages to be derived from having a sheltered coastline with most of the power extracted from the waves before they reach the shore. One possible advantage is that large-scale coastal fish farms could be set up in the calm region of water behind the power stations, providing an enormous and controllable new source of food for future generations. A further advantage is that, as with other renewable energy sources, there would be no heat pollution, and no chemical contamination of the environment.

Another kind of ocean power can be derived from tides in certain parts of the world. The Bay of Fundy in Canada, for example, which has the world's biggest tidal range due to the shape of the bay, is ideally suitable for harnessing tidal power, and a billion dollar tidal energy scheme, in which dams would trap the water and release it through hydro-electric turbines to generate electricity, is being planned. Britain's Severn Estuary, where the focussing properties of the English Channel produce very high tidal ranges, is the world's second best site for tidal power generation. And in France, on the river Rance, near St Malo, a small tidal power scheme has been in operation successfully for several years, proving the technology on a relatively small scale. Tidal power schemes are also potentially viable in many other countries which have coastal boundaries.

Tidal power schemes are based on a similar technology to existing hydro-electric schemes which provide some of the cheapest electricity available. Like wind and wave power, hydro-electric power is basically derived from solar energy: the Sun's heat evaporates water from the oceans, lifting it into the atmosphere. This forms rain which collects in reservoirs at high altitudes. In hydro-power schemes, the lakes and reservoirs are basically a means of storing the energy until it is needed. Energy is released from the water by allowing it to flow downwards with great force, and, in so doing, to turn turbines. The use of high-altitude reservoirs is also an effec-

Above
An artist's impression of Sir Christopher Cockerell's *Contour Raft* which effectively follows the contour of the wave. The snaking motion of the raft moves hydraulic pumps which drive the electric generators.

Opposite
Aerial view of the French *tidal power* project on the River Rance near St Malmo. Energy is harnessed by concentrating the tidal flow through openings in the barrier where hydro-electric turbines are situated. The pressure of water drives the turbines.

the buoy is driven upwards and then through pipes to the turbines. Yet another system, announced in 1978 by Dr Francis Farley, F.R.S., of the Royal Military College of Science, consists of two flat plates, linked together like an accordion, which face the waves and, acting as a pump, extract the energy produced as each wave pushes one plate towards the other.

A system which is in a very advanced stage of design and has already been tested on the Solent (the sea between the Isle of Wight and the southern coast of England) is the contouring raft designed by Sir Christopher Cockerell, inventor of the hovercraft. This system consists of a raft in several sections, each section joined to the next by hinges attached to hydraulic pumps. As waves pass, the raft snakes or contours over the surface of the water, putting the hinges in motion and powering the hydraulic pumps which drive the electric generators. During the

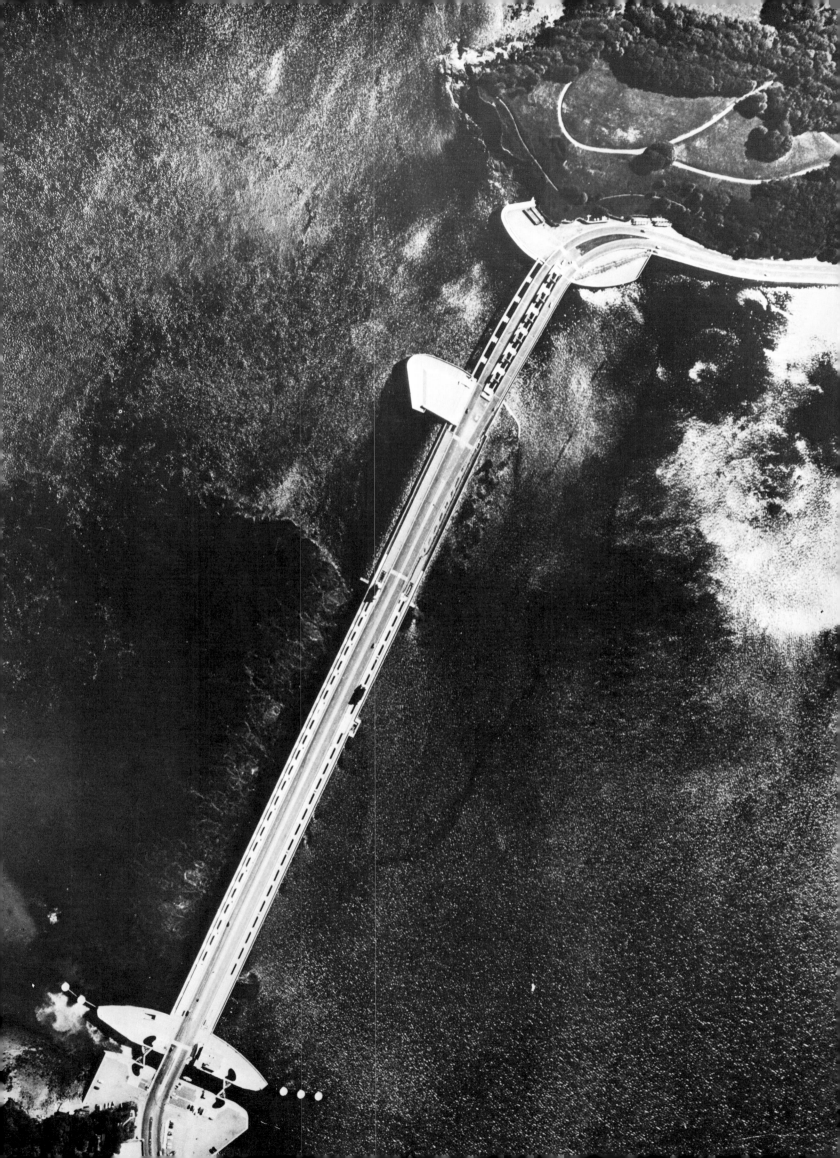

tive means of recycling electricity. When too much electricity is being generated, the excess can be used to pump water up to high altitude, from where it can be re-utilized.

Dams such as the Aswan High Dam in Egypt, and the Volta Dam in Ghana, have shown how this cheap hydro-electricity can transform a country's energy situation. In Ghana, for example, the Volta Dam provides far more electricity than the country's present-day needs, but yet more is still to be tapped. The output is currently justified only in terms of the need to smelt aluminium for foreign companies which managed to strike a bargain deal in return for building the dam, but during the next century, Ghana will have full rights to the total electricity production of the dam. This will make possible a large increase in industrial activities, and the country will thus be fully independant and expanding in terms of electricity production at a time when many other countries may be feeling the approach of austerity as the fossil fuels run low.

There is undoubtedly a great deal of scope throughout the world for expanding the use of hydro-electric power, though some places are more favoured than others. Potentially, any source of water in a mountainous region is capable of yielding hydro-power, but apart from the developing countries which at present consume only a relatively small amount of electricity, most countries will be able to derive only a minor proportion of their electrical needs from this source. However, these countries may be able to supplement this energy source by harnessing the Sun's power directly. By the next century it seems likely that a fairly diverse range of solar power equipment will be installed in many different countries, even those with temperate climates.

Many existing buildings already benefit from solar power to some extent: south-facing windows and walls provide a large proportion of heat input, though most existing buildings are not designed to take the maximum advantage of this, and often the heat received is lost almost as quickly as it is gained. But there are many experimental buildings, constructed by solar energy research groups all over the world, which are designed to take the maximum amount of energy from the Sun's rays, and retain as much of it as possible. Basic features of solar houses are that they have large areas of south-facing windows, preferably

Above
The highly reflective, curved metal plates on this *solar energy collector* cause the sun's rays to converge on the glass tube in the centre. Water or another suitable liquid is heated by the rays and circulated to utilize the energy. This device is part of the solar technology being tested at the Sandia Laboratories in Albuquerque, New Mexico

Left
The Compound Parabolic Concentrator (CPC), a solar energy collector, which is capable of concentrating the rays of the sun 10 times is now undergoing tests at the Argonne National Laboratory, near Chicago. Basically, the CPC acts like a solar funnel, forcing the collected light into the brightest possible concentration. This enables it to collect efficiently the diffuse light of a cloudy day as well as direct sunlight.

Opposite
The Ffestiniog *pumped storage hydro-electric power scheme* consists of two reservoirs, one above the other. When the generators are producing too much electricity, the excess can be used to pump water back up to the top reservoir, enabling the water to be reutilised.

Our dependence on fossil fuels and their limited availability has led to an intensive search for alternative sources. Early investigations have identified a range of possibilities covering nuclear fission and fusion processes, solar power and the release of energy from wind and water movements.

Considerable advances have already been made and although there are many difficulties which have yet to be overcome before we are able to exploit these possibilities on a global scale, such sights as this giant solar collector could become commonplace in the near future.

Left
Researchers at the Lawrence Livermore Laboratory in California construct an experimental shallow water *solar pond*. Such ponds have been shown to be highly promising devices for producing economical energy in the form of hot water and electricity.

Below
Solar One, designed by the Massachusetts Institute for Technology, is the first solar house with an active system for converting the sun's energy into electricity by means of solar cells (photovoltaic).

Opposite
The modern approach of the French to solar energy is demonstrated in the huge *solar furnace* at Odeillo in the Pyrenees. The sun's rays are reflected by two series of mirrors onto an area the size of a large cooking pot where temperatures of over 4,000°C (7,232°F) have been recorded.

inclined from the vertical to enable the Sun's rays to shine in directly; double-glazing to help keep the warmth inside once it has arrived; shutters to close over the windows at night; and very good insulation, resulting in heat-loss at a much slower rate than ordinary buildings. Solar houses often have heat storage systems such as very thick walls which can absorb excess heat during the day-time, preventing the house from getting too warm, and release it during the night time when the Sun is not available, and also often feature solar water heating panels: tanks filled with water which is warmed by the Sun's heat for use as domestic hot water. Solar heat can also be used to power air-conditioning units, making it possible to avoid using other sources of power when the electricity

demand for air-conditioning would otherwise be at its greatest. It is signifi-cant that the times of peak electricity demand in such cities as New York normally arise during the hottest parts of the year, mainly because of the need for air conditioning. (The problem is aggra-vated by the fact that many modern office and apartment blocks are designed to depend on continuous air-condition-ing or heating.)

One of the first solar houses was constructed in the late 1930s by Professor Hoyt C. Hottel of the Massachusetts Institute of Technology. A recent pioneer-ing design for a solar house which not only captures natural heat but also uses the Sun to generate electricity by means of solar cells is the so-called Solar One house, created by engineers at the University of

Delaware in the United States. By contrast, the Ryan House, developed with the help of the Berkeley Solar Group in California uses solar heat but not solar-powered electricity. This house features nearly 40 square metres of south-facing double-glazed windows as well as a similar area of solar panels for water heating placed in front of the house below the level of the windows.

A different application of the same principles is the magnificent solar power experiment which has been mounted by French scientists in the mountains near the French–Spanish border. It is a solar furnace consisting of two huge arrays of mirrors which concentrate the Sun's rays onto a volume the size of a large cooking pot. One array of mirrors is fixed onto the side of a building 40 metres high facing

Above

Two *solar photovoltaic systems*, located atop Mount Washington, New Hampshire, under test for long term performance in extreme climates. Data, such as power loss through varying amounts of snow and/or ice, snow shedding or melting, is shared with the main photovoltaic program.

Opposite

The agricultural application of photovoltaics (the direct conversion by a solar cell of the sun's rays into electricity) was tested in the summer of 1977 by the M.I.T. Laboratories in Lincoln, Mass. An experimental unit, generating approximately 25 kw peak power, was used to run an irrigation system and crop drying fans. The twenty-eight solar panels arranged in two rows, contained over 2,000 solar cell modules. Each panel was interconnected with inverters to allow alternating current (AC) as well as direct current (DC) motors to be tested; and with 85 kw hours lead acid battery storage (in the three caravans on right of panels) to maintain a constant power level. The irrigation system was used successfully to irrigate eighty acres of cornfields surrounding the reservoir and to dry the 12,000 bushels of grain which were harvested. The photovoltaic system gave constant electric power when needed with only 2 modules out of 2,000 failing to produce electricity.

north. The second array consists of sixty-five mirrors with a total area half the size of a football pitch. Each of these mirrors can rotate to follow the Sun during the day, so that its rays can be concentrated onto the north-facing mirrors which, in turn, are focussed onto the small volume which forms the solar furnace. The furnace produces 1,000 kilowatts of energy and temperatures of 4,000 degrees centigrade or even more.

Another alternative means of harnessing solar energy is to spread out a large area of solar cells which generate electricity directly. At present, such cells, which have been developed for use on space craft, are several hundred times too expensive to be used as an economical form of electricity generation on Earth, but in the United States, the semi-conductor industry is making a large effort to produce cheaper solar cells, and in Japan, the Toshiba Company are hoping to reduce the cost by a factor of one hundred or so by producing semi-conductor material in the form of a long strip. As has already been proven with other semi-conductor devices such as the transistor and the silicon chip, it is

expected that in a few decades or perhaps even sooner, prices may have fallen sufficiently to make solar cells a viable alternative source of electricity.

The best place to harness solar energy, whether by solar cells or by mirrors focussing the Sun's rays on to a furnace, is in Space where no clouds or atmosphere can reduce the intensity of the Sun's power. The American National Aeronautics and Space Administration is studying the possibility of putting a large satellite into high orbit around the Earth. It would have huge arms, spread out like sails, covered with solar cells. The electricity could be fed to a microwave generator which would beam the power down to Earth. The satellite could generate more power than some of the largest existing power stations on Earth. There would, of course, be problems such as ensuring that aircraft and wildlife were not destroyed by the intense beam of microwaves used to transfer the energy to Earth, but the advantages of such a system are immense. Space is such a perfect, clean, environment, that once the satellite is in orbit it should require almost no maintenance. In a high orbit,

such a satellite could capture the Sun's rays for most of the day, being eclipsed by the Earth's shadow for only an hour or so every day, and it would not interfere with the environment on Earth in the way in which huge solar collectors at ground level might.

One of the simplest methods of harnessing solar power, is to use it to grow plants which can then be converted into a variety of fuels. It has been estimated that plants harness ten times as much energy from the Sun as the world is currently consuming conventional fuels. Recently, Brazil has become the leading user of plant-derived energy, and in many parts of the country cars now use a mixture of 20% alcohol in their fuel. The alcohol, which is derived from the fermentation of sugar and other carbohydrate sources, is already saving a great deal of imported petroleum. Almost any plant having the ability to grow quickly can be used to produce liquid, gaseous, and solid fuels by fermentation or chemical processes. In Australia, five crops are being considered for this purpose: eucalyptus trees, casava, sugar cane, napier grass, and hibiscus, all of

which have the ability to yield large quantities of carbohydrate. In the United States, sugar cane is also a candidate, as are poplar trees. In temperate countries, maize, grasses, and rapidly growing indigenous bushes are all potential source materials for fuels. During the coming decades 'energy farms' may become a feature of the countryside, something which developing countries in particular may find particularly appealing. Many poorer countries still use wood as a principal source of energy, and whereas there may not be sufficient wood to provide enough fuel for future generations, the energy farms, concentrating on the cultivation of high carbohydrate yielding plants, could fill the gap. Harvesting would be relatively labour-intensive, making such systems ideal for poorer countries with high unemployment.

Apart from all of these alternative applications of solar energy exists the possibility of harnessing the process by which all plants convert the Sun's rays into carbon compounds: photosynthesis. Professor David Hall of King's College, London University, has produced hydro-

gen in the test tube from the chloroplasts of plant leaves, the plant cells which carry out photosynthesis. Under man's control, photosynthesis, during which chloroplasts split water (chemically consisting of oxygen and hydrogen) into its constituents, yielding gaseous oxygen and hydrogen, could provide energy for the future. Work by Dr John Benemann at the University of California also suggests that in the future such processes could provide commercially useful quantities of hydrogen. The project was given another boost recently when the 1978 Nobel Prize for Chemistry was awarded to Dr Peter Mitchell of the Glynn Research Institute in Cornwall, England, for his theory concerning the mechanism within living cells whereby energy is transferred from one part of the living organism to another. Mitchell's theory involves a new concept called 'proticity', equivalent to electricity, but concerned with the motion of protons – positively charged units of matter, which are actually electrically charged hydrogen atoms. By putting forward a very clear theory of how energy is transferred within living systems, Mitchell has

The Pacific Gas and Electric Company's generating units (units 3 and 4 shown here) are producing increasing quantities of electricity from *geothermal steam*. The current capacity of 608,000 kw from twelve units is to be raised to 908,000 kw by the addition of new units under construction; by mid-1980 this will be enough electricity to supply 1 million houses.

paved the way for a better understanding of the energy processes. Conceivably, this could lead to practical systems for harnessing the Sun's energy through plant cells. Mitchell himself says that the understanding of proticity may help improve existing electronic systems as well as helping scientists understand biological organisms. In fact, it has been suggested that joining together semi-conductor electronics and natural energy-harnessing processes such as photosynthesis could one day yield electrical energy directly from the Sun's rays.

A huge, largely untapped, source of energy lies beneath every one of us, wherever we are in the world: below ground. As far as is known, the centre of the Earth is very hot, and, certainly, volcanoes indicate that temperatures hot

enough to melt rocks exist deep within the Earth's crust. In most places, it is necessary to drill only 2 or 3 kilometres down into the ground to reach rock temperatures capable of boiling water. Harnessing power from naturally produced steam is the simplest and easiest method of producing power from this so-called geothermal energy. The technique is quite an old one. Geothermal steam has been used to generate electricity from the beginning of the twentieth century at Larderello, near Florence in Italy. At The Geysers, a place not far from San Francisco in the United States, where high pressure steam, the result of water being vaporised at great depth by hot rocks, escapes naturally from the ground, the goethermal power station which was constructed is now the largest of its kind in the world. It uses the steam directly to drive turbines and generate electricity. In many other parts of the world, hot water can be obtained naturally from deep within the ground, and often from quite near the surface. In France, the Paris Basin has a rock formation which lends itself very well to the exploitation of naturally occurring hot water. The rocks are largely porous and bear water. It is only necessary to bore a few kilometres into the ground to reach water hot enough for central heating. This has now been done, and some buildings in Paris are now being heated by water from the ground. Two boreholes are needed, one to extract the water, and another, situated some distance away from the first, to deliver the cool, waste water back to the ground. In one scheme, costing about 5 million U.S. dollars to install, the natural waters deliver 80% of the heat required during an average year.

The geothermal heat comes free once the installation has been completed. Nevertheless engineers work out the cost of the heat in terms of the installation and maintenance costs spread over the expected lifetime of the system. This price is still lower than for other central heating systems which have to use fuel. Currently, many different countries are progressing with plans to make use of this type of geothermal heat during the coming decades, but such schemes draw on only a small fraction of the heat available from within our planet.

In most parts of the world, the temperature rises by at least 30 degrees centigrade for every kilometre's depth into the ground. In places where the rocks are porous, hot water can often be found naturally, or water can be introduced into the rocks. But more than 90% of the rocks in the Earth's crust are

At La Caravelle, an apartment complex in Villneuve-La-Garenne, Paris, the 1,700 apartments are heated by hot water pumped from underground. Six hundred such installations would save the French 900,000 tonnes (1 million tons) of oil a year.

Diagram of the *geothermal energy plant* at The Geysers in California. In the natural process, rain water seeps through fissures (1) and permeable rock (2) until it reaches bedrock (3) and forms an underground lake. The bedrock is heated by the magma below it (4) which in turn heats the water and converts it to steam. This steam is usually vented on the surface through fissures forming a hot spring or fumarole (5). The Pacific Gas and Electric Company have tapped this energy by sinking two boreholes into the ground (6 & 7). Water is passed down one borehole (6) which is then turned to steam and pumped up the second borehole (7) to a generating unit (8).

impervious to water, and contain almost no trapped water at all. Furthermore, most rocks are not good heat conductors, and in order to extract this heat it is necessary to make thousands of small channels in the rocks through which water can be pumped. Recent experiments in the United States and Britain give grounds for considerable optimism concerning such exploitation of geothermal heat. At the Los Alamos Scientific Laboratory in New Mexico, U.S.A., scientists are pumping water at very high pressures into boreholes with the aim of cracking open thousands of small fissures in dry rocks. After cracking the rocks, water can be pumped in, heated by the rocks, and then extracted from a different borehole. The Los Alamos group has already shown that this can be done in granite at depths of 3 kilometres, where temperatures reach 200 degrees centigrade. Some very encouraging supporting work for this project has come from Britain. In Cornwall, where tin mining has been a traditional activity for many years, Dr Tony Batchelor, of the School of Mines at Camborne, has hit upon an improved method of cracking the hot, dry rocks. His technique is to drill a hole, and then to detonate a small explosive charge at the bottom. This initiates the cracking process which then continues under the action of highly pressurised

injections of water. An added advantage in the Cornish situation is that the water dissolves valuable minerals such as copper from the rocks, and thus forms a method of extraction which could be increasingly valuable as world supplies of many minerals run low. The geothermal heat then comes as an added bonus which could make all the difference to the profitability of such an operation.

More than twenty countries now have plans to exploit geothermal energy on an increasing scale in the decades ahead. The United States, which is already generating more than 500 megawatts of geothermally produced electricity (equivalent to about half the output of a modern nuclear power station) will be capable of generating forty times this amount (20,000 megawatts) by the year 2,000. Mexico may also equal the geothermal generating capacity of the United States by the turn of the century, and in terms of the proportion of geothermal energy consumed nationally, could then become a leading producer. But the countries with the most accessible potential for growth in this area are those like Japan, with active volcanic resources (volcanoes bring geothermal heat very close to the Earth's surface). By the next century, Japan could generate a staggering 50,000 megawatts of electricity through geothermal exploitation

alone, which would bring Japan closer to self-sufficiency in terms of energy.

Before all of the technology relating to these natural, renewable forms of energy can be exploited on a scale large enough to be effective, the world will have to rely on the presently available methods, but with tight controls on the conservation of our precious resources. For example, there is a great deal of unused heat energy available on the surface of the Earth. Regretably, most power stations are very wasteful of energy. A coal fired station, for example, converts at best hardly more than a third of the heat energy from coal into electricity. For every kilowatt of electricity produced, there are usually 2 kilowatts of waste heat. Most power stations get rid of the waste heat by means of heat exchanging devices such as cooling towers. In some places, where the power stations are built conveniently close to towns and cities, the heat is made available for domestic and industrial use (district heating), but because most power stations have been sited, for environmental reasons, away from the centres of towns and cities, it has in the past been uneconomical to pipe supplies of steam or hot water to the metropolitan areas. However, as supplies of fossil fuels run low and as prices skyrocket, the economics of using waste heat from power stations is becoming a great deal more attractive.

A power generating system, which was designed from the outset to provide almost as much energy in the form of heat as it does in the form of electricity, is presently servicing part of the English town of Hereford. Compared to units which do not distribute waste heat, this system's diesel generator produces 15 megawatts of electrical power and 13 megawatts of heat (in the form of steam) for local industry, almost doubling its overall efficiency. Similarly, the Danish coastal town of Fredericia, the first community in the world to obtain domestic central heating by using industrial waste heat, is also doubling its efficiency. This has come about through the co-operation between Superfloss, a locally situated chemical company, and the council authority which usually provides heating from a central boiler house. Superfloss, which supplies oil for the town's boiler, normally disposes of millions of gallons of hot water produced during the manufacturing process, but as a result of the agreement, Superfloss is converting the community's heating installations and re-directing this water for domestic heating use. Half of this heat is provided free of charge. The other half is billed at a rate comparable to the current cost of oil, which amply covers the $6 million cost of conversion. Conse-

During *coal liquefaction*, a process which is under development in both Europe and the U.S., the action of a solvent (for example, steam or methanol) at an elevated temperature depolymerises coal into low molecular weight fragments. These then dissolve in the solvent to form liquid coal, which is roughly equivalent to crude oil.

In the diagram, the solvent (1) is passed to the coal seam (2) and liquefaction takes place. The liquid coal (3) is then pumped to the surface and purified in a processing plant (4). Pump house (5) and storage tank (6).

quently, the company can save the cost of 12,000 tons of oil (half the town's pre-conversion consumption), enabling it to produce fertilizers at a more competitive price, and enabling each household to reduce its central heating bill by at least $200 per year. When these systems are applied to the largest power stations and industrial complexes, the potential savings of both fuel and energy will be enormous.

As well as boosting the efficiency of power stations by using waste heat, it is also possible to improve the efficiency of the fuel-burning process itself. Due to the coming fossil fuel shortage, it is likely that high quality fuels will be exhausted long before the lower grade fuels such as low grade coal, and the residue called bunkering fuel, which is left over when the best quality constituents of crude oil have been removed. But a breakthrough in the technology of burning low grade fuels has been achieved with the development of the so-called fluidised bed, a furnace that contains a bed of sand through which a current of air is blown to keep the grains of sand continually in motion, like a boiling liquid. This is an ideal burning surface for almost any combustible fuel. The Central Electricity Generating Board in Britain is hoping to demonstrate a fluidised bed power station in the near future, and a variety of individual engineering companies are currently developing fluidised bed furnaces. Some designs are even capable of producing low polluting energy from domestic or industrial rubbish. The Deborah Coatings Company in County Durham, England, has developed a system which simultaneously disposes of industrial rubbish and provides steam heat for industrial use. The Coatings Company claims that they can pay for the system's installation costs within two years by saving fuel costs and rubbish disposal charges. Looking to the future, it could soon be a simple matter to reduce fuel bills and dispose of rubbish simultaneously by installing small fluidised bed incinerators into apartment and office blocks. The fluidised bed produces such efficient burning that almost all pollution can be eliminated, even in the case of fuels which contain impurities, such as sulphur, by the adding of minerals such as lime to the mixture being burned.

Most adult Londoners can remember the days of the 'pea souper' fogs which used to beset the city. These were caused by industrial activities and the use of coal for heating homes. Indeed, the fogs began with the industrial revolution centuries earlier. Until the 1950s, the River Thames was so heavily polluted that no fish could survive in it. The problem was so severe

The *Hot Dry Rock Geothermal Energy* project was started in 1970 by U.S. scientists who believed that considerable amounts of energy could be extracted from naturally hot, underground rock by creating an artificial geothermal reservoir. It has been estimated that the geothermal energy available in 64 cu. km (40 cu. m) of granite is equivalent to the energy from 12 million barrels of oil, or nearly the total energy used by the U.S. in 1977.

In 1977, the experiment, in which cold water was forced into one deep borehole, through fractured rock, and then extracted from another borehole, was successfully completed at Los Alamos, New Mexico. After twenty hours of pumping, the water temperature was 265°F (130°C) and still rising. The scientists plan to expand the fracture by further drilling and then to construct a 100 mw experimental plant, which would produce enough electricity for 10,000 houses. The picture shows one of the drilling rigs used to bore the deep holes at Los Alamos.

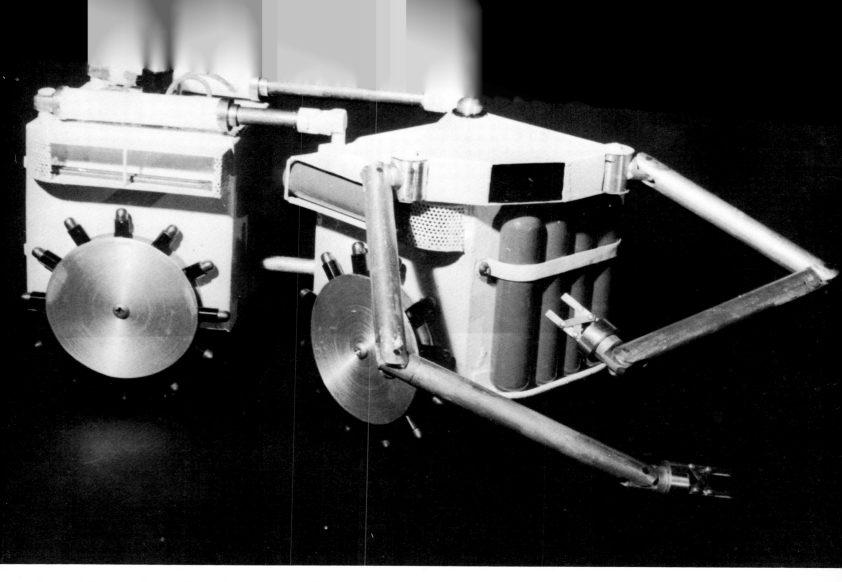

that sulphurous fumes from the river made life unpleasant for anybody living or working near the Thames. In the last two decades, however, the city's air pollution has been cleared largely by the passing of strict laws which almost totally prohibited smoke from the city. Cleaner fuels such as gas and electricity have been substituted for coal with the result that the pea souper fog is no longer seen, the capital enjoys a great deal more sunshine than before, and the River Thames now boasts 100 varieties of fish. However, with the advent of these new, cleaner, fuel-burning processes, it is likely that coal will again be a major energy resource for a long time to come.

One of the encouraging features of coal derived energy is that new reserves are being discovered continually. This is also one reason why no one can confidently predict when all supplies will be exhausted. It is known that there is a great deal more coal underground than can be extracted by existing manual techniques (many seams being too narrow for men to enter). At present, because miners have to dig deeper to extract the less accessible coal, the potential for accidents is increasing. One solution to this problem may well be the remote control coal miner designed by professor Meredith Thring of London University. At present, the principal objection to using such machines, which

could perform all of the underground coal mining tasks currently performed by humans, is the cost, but it is likely that for the deep, inaccessible coal seams they would be no more expensive to use than humans. With robots, a great deal of expense could be saved by reducing the need to make mines as safe as possible: underground structures would not need to be so robust; there would be no need to ventilate them; and neither would the mines require such extensive precautions against fire and flooding. Machines capable of working in a flooded mine could be designed as well.

Britain's National Coal Board is also developing alternative methods of extracting coal without the need for men to work underground. At the Mining Research and Development Establishment at Bretby in England, Coal Board scientists are working on methods of turning coal into liquids or gases underground and pumping it to the surface. Combustible gases can be formed from coal underground by setting fire to the coal seam. The force of the heat drives gas out of the coal and forces it to the surface. At present, this method presents some problems: the difficulty of setting fire to the coal, the variable quality of the gas produced, and the uneconomical costs. But when alternative fuels become more costly, this method of gasification may

Model of a *remote control coal miner* designed by Professor Thring of Queen Mary College, London. These automatic machines could perform many of the jobs hazardous to human miners, as they are not troubled by poisonous gases or water.

become widespread.

Another method, liquiefaction of coal underground, can be achieved by adding steam or other solvents such as methanol to the coal seam. The resulting liquid, which contains dissolved coal and which is roughly equivalent to crude oil, can then be processed in coal refineries to extract all of the compounds and chemicals, including petroleum, which we currently obtain from crude oil.

Transport and Travel

Just as computer control for homes becomes a possibility with the continuing fall in price of all micro-electronic systems, so automobile control by computer is likely to begin in a big way soon. The year 2000 promises to provide a far more diverse range of vehicles for personal mobility than is available today. These would incorporate a considerable number of electronic devices which conserve energy and increase safety.

Human drivers have proved themselves incapable of avoiding road accidents and traffic jams, but the computer will soon be able to eliminate most of these problems. Future drivers should be able to benefit from a microwave radar system, linked to an automobile computer, which can detect the positions and speeds of other vehicles. The computer can then interpret these findings and automatically control the car's braking, in order to maintain a safe distance from the vehicle ahead, or to give the driver information such as whether oncoming cars are around the bend, and whether it is safe to pass. The single function of automatically controlling vehicle-following distances, could eliminate most of the now familiar multiple vehicle crashes experienced on highways and motorways, especially during dangerous weather conditions. The computer would calculate safe distances, not only on the basis of speed information, but through information supplied by short-range radio signals from roadside transmitters concerning the frictional quality of the road. The driver would still be responsible for steering the vehicle in such systems, but he would be able to relax at the wheel knowing that the automobile computer can override any potentially dangerous habits he may have. In ad-

Opposite top
Cross-section of the proposed London underway, housing roads, mono-railways, travelators and car parks, to alleviate the traffic problems of the city centre.

Below
Computer-controlled vehicles will be far safer than those under present-day, all-manual control. Equipped with electrical servo systems for activating vehicle controls, as well as miniature radio transmitters and receivers for communicating with roadside signalling systems and other vehicles, the computer-controlled car would receive and react to advance information about traffic jams, maximum cornering speeds, minimum following distances and whether or not the road is clear for passing. Having the facility to instruct the car to drive as fast as possible, or to conserve fuel, a driver would be able to leave the driving to the computer until he arrived at his destination.

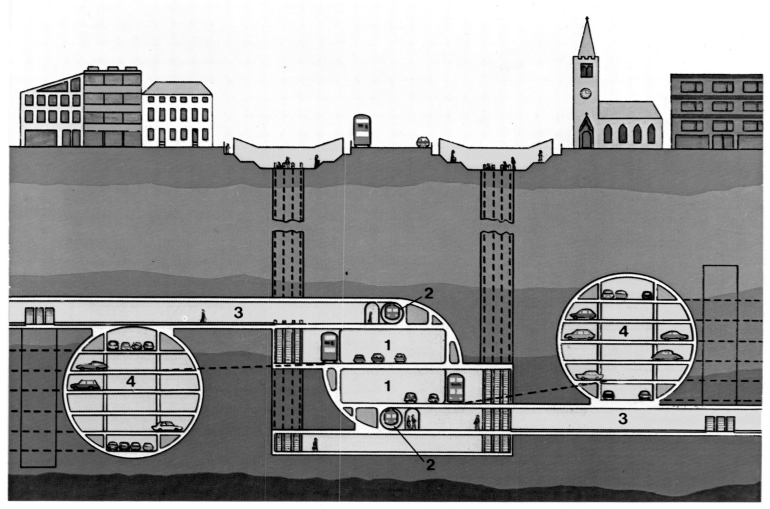

Right
Model of proposed underground traffic
tunnel for the *London Underway* scheme.
The motor car is an inextricable part of life in
many parts of the world, as are the problems
it brings: air and noise pollution, accidents,
traffic congestion, and lack of adequate
parking areas. One solution which has been
proposed by the London architectural and
planning firm of Covell Matthews &
Partners, is to install underground tunnels.
This would clear the urban area of most
through traffic, leaving surface roads for
local use only. Further advantages would be
the lack of delays caused by traffic lights,
pedestrian crossings, and bad weather, as
well as the increased surface land area
available for building construction, and cost
savings on road maintenance and traffic
control.

The tunnels would be about 18 m (60 ft)
in diameter and built in four sections by
remotely controlled diggers approximately
30.5 m (100 ft) below the surface. They
would accommodate two sections of three
fast traffic lanes and one slow or breakdown
lane for each direction; two sections for
monorail and moving pavement mass transit
systems; and tubes for blowpipe transport of
freight and other goods. The tunnel system
would incorporate feeder entry/exit points,
cross-over intersections provided by
secondary tunnels, link-up systems with
other forms of transport, and parking
facilities with closed-circuit television
security systems.

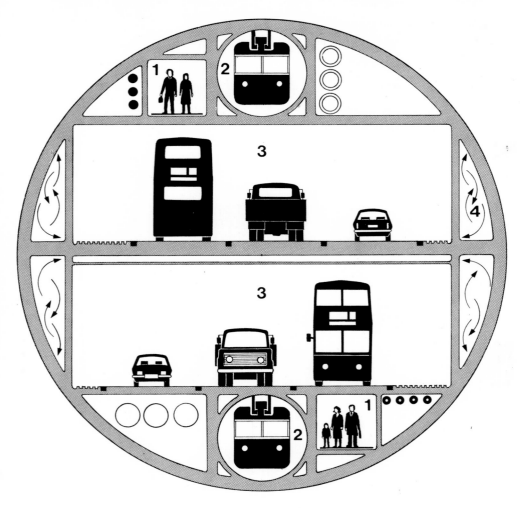

dition, traffic signals in towns could incorporate short-range radio transmitters capable of communicating directly with the automobile computer. Recommended speeds for maintaining a smooth flow of traffic, and advanced warnings of traffic jams, could help the driver complete his journey without the frustrating disorder that has been a distinct feature of twentieth century driving.

The ultimate safety measure, however, is automatic vehicle guidance systems such as those that work by means of cables buried in the road, which transmit guidance information to the automobile computer. This is likely to be initiated on trunk roads and highways and subsequently in towns and cities. On entering the highway, the automobile computer would instruct the driver to switch to automatic guidance. Under such a system, the driver would be able to safely go to sleep until reaching the end of the road. All of the basic requirements for automatic vehicle guidance and collision avoidance have already been developed. Microwave radars, mini computers and microprocessors, electrical servo systems for activating vehicle controls, and miniature radio transmitters and receivers for communicating information remotely have all been available for several years. The problem has been the cost of installing such systems. Without government legislation, motor manufacturers have been reluctant to undertake the

investment necessary for incorporating such devices, but it seems likely that because the costs are continually falling, many countries will soon pass legislation for the installation of at least part of such systems in order to avoid road accidents and improve traffic flow.

'Will computer controlled cars be fun to drive?' The answer should be *Yes*. Although practically every competitive aspect of driving can be removed by automatic systems, the ride could still be exhilerating. When the driver sets his computer to give the least possible journey time, the ride could be far more exciting than under human control – and far safer. The computer could quickly calculate maximum cornering speeds and minimum following distances, and, with traffic information remotely transmitted from roadside monitoring units, the car would not need to slow down when the road ahead could not be seen. At lower speeds, such as when the computer is set to produce maximum fuel efficiency, the driver could safely pay attention to the surrounding sights, without having to worry about operating the controls.

Perhaps the most radical change in road vehicles will concern the engines themselves. The familiar internal combustion engine may well be in decline, giving way to other forms of propulsion such as electric motors and even steam power. When traditional fossil fuels run out, many of the internal combustion

engines remaining in use might be converted to run on a variety of alternative fuels: natural gas, petrol derived from coal, methyl alcohol (methanol), ethyl alcohol, and even hydrogen. There could also be vehicles with two or more engines, and radically altered vehicle designs which maximise fuel efficiency. At present, the British Petroleum Company and Britain's National Coal Board are collaborating in studies aimed at producing liquid fuels from coal by refinery techniques similar to those used in the oil industry. They have set up an experimental coal refinery, and in 1977 the new fuel was used for the first time to power an Automobile Association patrol car. Synthetic gasoline is relatively costly to produce, especially when compared with methanol which can also be derived from coal. Methanol can be used as fuel, and its use would be in keeping with energy conservation measures in the future, because waste heat such as that from nuclear reactors can be used to combine steam and coal to produce very high yields of methanol.

Research has also shown that hydrogen in liquid form could eliminate the problem of exhaust fumes. Dr Lawrence Jones of the University of Michigan in the United States who has studied the use of hydrogen for automobiles, has pointed out that most trials of its use have been completely successful. Hydrogen burns to produce water and no other pollutants and can be produced from a variety of processes: from the action of electricity on water, by modified natural processes such as photosynthesis, or chemically with the help of waste heat from nuclear and other types of power stations. The only drawback of liquid hydrogen is that it has to be stored at very low temperatures, and so specially insulated tanks are needed in hydrogen powered automobiles. Another method of storing hydrogen is by combining it chemically with another substance which releases the gas when needed. Both methods may well be in use by the year 2000, and it is very possible that hydrogen will become the main portable source of power.

Electric road vehicles may be yet another answer to many of our transportation needs, but before the electric battery has been perfected there may be a range of hybrid propulsion systems. At London's Queen Mary College, a hybrid car, which has been built experimentally, combines an electric motor for accelerating with a small diesel engine. The diesel engine, on which the car cruises, also recharges the battery, readying it for the next acceleration. The Bosch Company in Germany and General Motors in the United States are also experimenting with such hybrid designs. The

Opposite
Cross section of a motorway tunnel in the *London Underway* scheme. (1) travelator, (2) monorail, (3) three-lane highway with a breakdown lane, (4) air ducts.

Left
The diesel/electric hybrid engine, designed by Mr. A. Bolandi of Queen Mary College, London University, promises to reduce the fuel consumption of present-day vehicles by 50% or even more, enabling a vehicle to carry enough fuel in the tank for over several hundred miles. The diesel engine, on which the vehicles cruises, also recharges the battery of the electric engine, which is used for acceleration.

Below
The batteries of electric road vehicles are extremely heavy and cumbersome and need to be recharged after short distances. However, lighter batteries are constantly being developed and should eventually aid the proliferation of efficient, pollution-free, silent, electric vehicles.

Many of today's transportation systems were conceived in a very different world from that of the present, and have evolved by adaptation and modification ever since. The rapidly changing needs of society, and the problems imposed by limited resources suggest that we are nearing the time for a re-appraisal of existing facilities.

The basic considerations of speed and economy have not changed very much, but the degree required in each case has outstripped current technolgoy in some measure.

The illustration shows some of the possibilities already being investigated, including an electromagnetically propelled train running through vacuum tubes and capable of speeds up to 500 km (300 mi) per hour. New materials and techniques have led to a fresh examination of airships as a safe and convenient form of travel and the background illustrates what a local airship terminal could look like. The unmanned modular taxis in the foreground run along guidance strips set in the road surface and can operate individually or linked in groups to carry passengers to their destinations.

diesel-electric engine promises to give far greater fuel economy than the diesel engine alone, reducing fuel consumption by a factor of one half or even more.

The ultimate solution, however, the perfection of the silent, efficient, and pollution-free electric vehicle, should be well under way by the year 2000. The great advantage of electricity is that power stations can convert any source of energy into electricity and that it can easily be used for a diversity of transport needs. At present, the electric road vehicle suffers the disadvantage of requiring a very heavy battery which needs to be charged even after quite short journeys. Nevertheless, even with this limitation, which is continually being reduced as better, lighter batteries are developed, the electric vehicle will be able to fulfill most of the needs of the motorist in the future.

Research to improve the conventional lead-acid battery is also going on all over the world, but it might very well be surpassed by a different type of battery, the sodium-sulphur battery, which has already been developed. The sodium-sulphur battery uses molten sodium and sulphur as the electrodes, and offers at least a five-to-one advantage over lead-acid batteries in terms of weight and space. The main drawback of this battery is that it has to operate at a temperature higher than 300 degrees centigrade. If, therefore, sodium-sulphur batteries are to be supplied for commercial use, since a collision could cause the release of potentially poisonous and highly inflammable mixtures of sodium and sulphur into the environment, a completely sealed, collision-proof unit would have to be produced.

The future motorist may leave his battery-driven electric car on charge when not in use, charging it from the mains at home, from charger points at parking spaces, or perhaps even from city parking meters. A novel possibility is that the car may be modular: composed of several detachable units, each one sufficiently powerful to transport a single person. Even so, it is most likely that the future motorist will tend to use the electric car for short-distance travel only, relying on other forms of transport for longer journeys.

Paradoxically, one of the oldest and cheapest forms of personal transportation, the bicycle, may grow in popularity. Although it doesn't offer the comfort of alternative vehicles, the bicycle is the most supremely efficient device of all. It uses renewable, natural energy, and converts well over nine-

Opposite top
The electric bicycle, which is powered by a rechargeable battery, could well become a widely-used means of urban transportation.

Opposite below
Magnetically-levitated vehicles, like this one designed by Professor B. V. Jayawant of Sussex University in England, may soon provide efficient, pollution-free mass-transportation for inter-urban travelling.

Below
Electric buses are already being used for short-distance travel in many countries. Electric vehicles are so economically viable that their eventual wide-spread use is likely.

tenths of the energy from the propulsion unit, a human being, into power available at the road wheels (in stark contrast to the internal combustion engine which manages only a few percent of the chemical energy available from fuel converted into driving torque). Furthermore, the ingenious design of the bicycle, which provides the ideal gearing to enable the rider to use his energy to the best advantage, produces an overall efficiency which is at least five times greater than walking. For the same expenditure of energy, a rider can travel at least five times as far on a bicycle than when walking, and go three or four times faster. So we would expect cities of the future to help cyclists by constructing segregated cycle tracks to avoid the danger of mixing the vulnerable two-wheel rider with heavy traffic.

But not everybody, of course, enjoys pedalling: for them the electric bicycle offers the ideal compromise. First available in 1978, this conveyance has a special electric motor, mounted in the front-wheel hub, which is powered by a rechargable battery in the saddle-bag.

The most hopeful scenario of city life at the beginning of the next century is that public transport systems will have developed and expanded to provide everyone with mobility, almost on a level with that which car owners enjoy today. Public transport should give an even better service than the automobile, which is prone to traffic delays, parking problems, mechanical failure, accidents and theft. Short-distance travel, such as within shopping centres, airport and rail terminals and inside large building complexes, may be facilitated by the widespread use of moving pavements, which have been in use for several years. Their main disadvantage is slow speed if installations are much more than 100 metres in length.

However, a new high speed moving pavement has been developed by Dunlop Ltd. This Dunlop 'Speedway' unit allows passengers to step on at the same speed as conventional moving pavements, but then accelerate in a curved path to five times the entry speed for the main part of their journey. Passengers, who may stand still or walk, are then automatically decelerated to the slow speed before stepping off the unit.

For journeys within town centres beyond the practical range of the moving pavements, cities may be equipped with Minitrams. Developed in Britain during the 1970s, these electrically driven computer-controlled cars, which can carry up to twenty people, have rubber pneumatic wheels and run on a concrete, possibly overhead track. The Minitram's mini-computer 'driver' receives

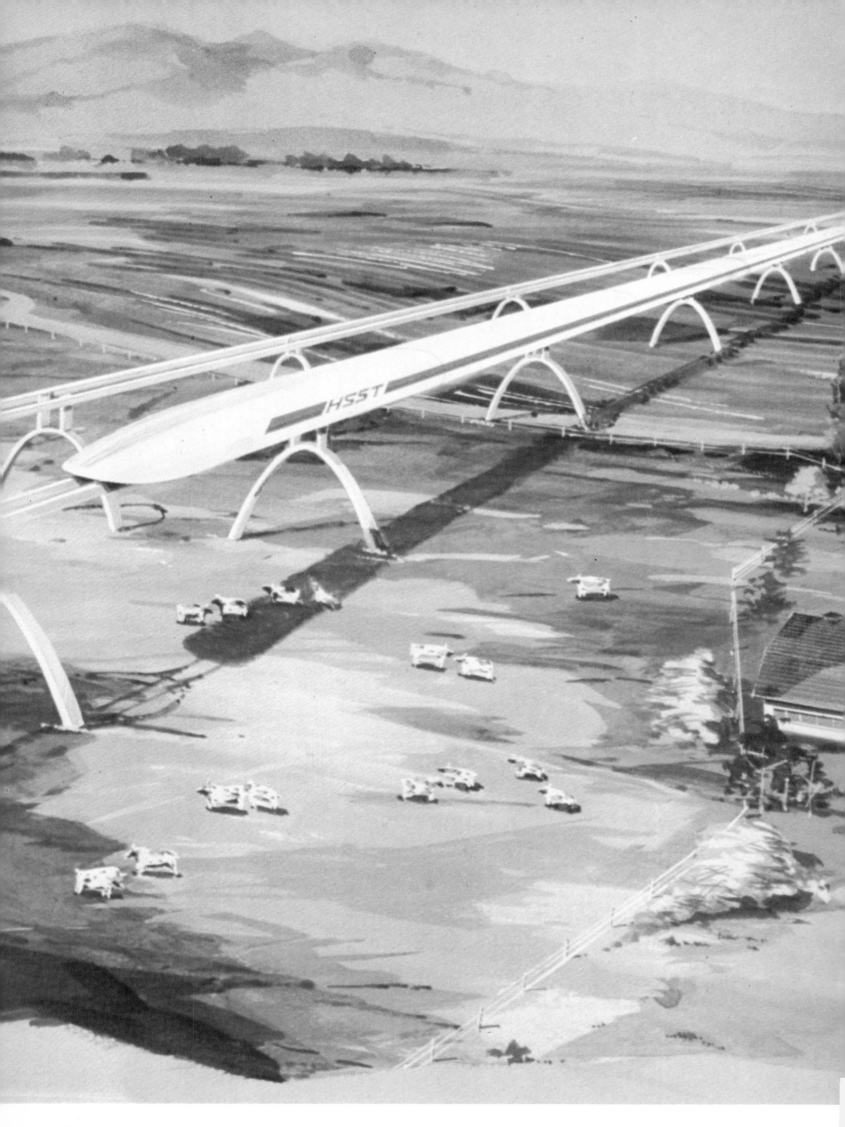

instructions about speed, the route it should take and where to stop, from aerials erected alongside the track. These are connected to a central computer that can co-ordinate the signalling for a large network of Minitrams. The cars would be able to travel at over 60 kilometres an hour with gaps of only five seconds between successive vehicles.

A further development of the Minitram concept is the self-routing taxi, sometimes called Cabtrack. The future urban traveller could step into this small taxi cab, perhaps big enough for only two passengers, and, by means of a dialled or punched-in code, instruct it to drive to the destination desired. Cabtrack stations would be placed every 200 metres, and special arrangements of track structure would make it possible for each individual cab to by-pass intermediate stations during a journey. Under a complex computer control, large numbers of Cabtrack taxis could be co-ordinated to transport individual passengers almost door to door from departure point to destination, offering almost the same service as a present-day taxi.

The pattern of long distance travel in the year 2000 may well depend on how well urban travel systems have developed. Automobiles have tradition-

ally provided a means of medium-distance travel for many people as well as an efficient method of travelling within towns and cities, but when the advantages of using them in towns are outweighed by efficient urban transport systems, cars may then be replaced for longer distance journeys.

The traveller of the future is likely to take the train for journeys of anything up to 1,000 kilometres provided there are no unbridged stretches of water to be crossed. His train could travel at over 250 kilometres per hour if it is one of the new generation of high speed trains running on ordinary track. Britain, France and Japan are currently leading the world in the development of high speed trains. In Japan, the new Tokaido Line was constructed between Tokyo and Osaka carrying trains which cover the 500 kilometre journey in little more than three hours. The track was specially built to high standards of alignment to make speeds of more than 200 kilometres per hour possible. The French 'TGV' (Train à Grande Vitesse), currently under development, should average 240 kilometres per hour on a new track being laid between Paris and Lyons. The British Advanced Passenger Train (APT) adopts

Opposite
Model for Japan's *high-speed monorail* train system.

Above
Travelling on Japan's Tokaido Line, the *high speed bullet train* can cover the 500 km (300 m) journey between Tokyo and Osaka in just over three hours. The track was specially built to allow speeds of more than 200 km (120 m) per hour.

a different philosophy from the Japanese and French supertrains. It is designed to run on ordinary track at 250 kilometres per hour, making it possible to speed-up every long distance route without rebuilding existing track. The Advanced Passenger Train has carriages of lightweight construction, and greatly improved suspension, which tilt on curves for improved passenger comfort. On the Japanese, French and British trains, a great deal of research has been undertaken to solve the problem of keeping the wheels accurately aligned with the rail. It is not often realised that the flanges on the inner sides of train wheels almost never touch the rail. They are only necessary for keeping the train on the rails at very low speeds and while negotiating tight bends during shunting. The modern supertrains also had to be designed so that at full speed the flanges never touch the rail. Otherwise, derailment could take place. This has been one of the most crucial difficulties to overcome because instabilities of motion can build up at these very high speeds which tend to throw the train violently from side to side. Ultimately, these instabilities pose a practical limit to the speeds attainable by steel-wheeled vehicles on

rail. So it is no coincidence that the Japanese, French and British designs all promise to travel at no more than about 250 kilometres per hour, although this practical limit may be raised yet again by continuing development. However, wheeled trains will probably have to give way eventually to different forms of tracked vehicles for travel at significantly higher speeds.

Trains of the early twenty-first century, running on a new type of track, may reach well over 500 kilometres per hour, making it possible to travel to most parts of a country the size of Britain or France in less than two hours. These are the magnetically levitated hovertrains: tracked vehicles which hover by magnetic repulsion 30 centimetres or so above a metal strip (the track) propelled like a surf-board riding along a 'magnetic river' as one engineer has described the system. British Rail and the German firm Thyssen Henschel are both working on magnetic levitation in which magnetic repulsion is induced between the vehicle and the metal track. Currently, however, both governments are unwilling to finance development of very high speed magnetically levitated vehicles, partly because conventional wheel-on-rail

Right
The conceptual *EDS magnetically levitated vehicle*
A: Cross section. B and C: schematic diagram of suspension. D: Cross section of EET magnetically levitated vehicle.
(1) passenger compartment; (2) secondary suspension; (3) lower frame; (4) lift magnet; (5) guide and propulsion magnet; (6) clamping winding; (7) reaction rails and LSM (linear synchrous motor) winding; (8) emergency guide and support.

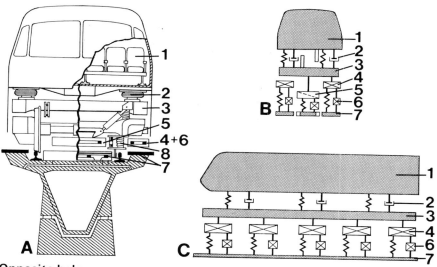

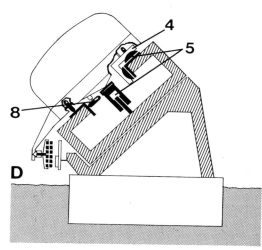

Opposite below

The experimental *EET magnetically levitated train* is being developed by the Siemens Co. in Erlangen, Germany. Magnetic levitation offers the possibility of increasing the speed of tracked vehicles to 500 km (300 m) per hour. The train's linear induction motor, which works in conjunction with superconducting (s.c.) magnets on board, and which is one of the largest of its kind, provides the necessary thrust to overcome air and electrodynamic drag, as well as to accelerate the vehicle and fascilitate ascents. The train's static load is supported by twenty s.c. magnets which react with aluminium strips mounted on the track. The magnets are distributed in pairs along the vehicle with spacings which match the uneven weight distribution of the vehicle. This also takes into account the longitudinal profile of lateral forces caused by side winds when leaving a tunnel or passing another vehicle.

The s.c. magnets are cooled by a forced flow of liquid and gaseous helium which is continuously filtered in and recovered by a decentralized refrigerator system on board each vehicle section.

Below 80 km (48 m) per hour, the vehicle is supported and guided by a conventional wheel-and-rail system. The transition from rolling to levitated mode is accomplished by raising or lowering the lift magnets hydraulically.

All primary components (bogies, and lift and propulsion magnets and their cold boxes) are mounted under a strong 'lower frame' on which the passenger compartment and other auxilliary equipment is mounted through the secondary suspension system's controllable air cushions.

At present, a 100 tonne (120 ton), 200-seat vehicle consisting of two equal sections coupled together, making up an overall length of 50 m (18.3 ft) is under design by the Siemens Company. In tests, a clearance of 100 mm (4 in) between the track surface and the bottom of the train was achieved at speeds of up to 120 km (72 mi) per hour.

systems still promise a great deal of improvement on present day rail speeds. Ultimately, the hovertrain principle offers a speed of over 500 kilometres per hour, and possibly even faster than this. Indeed, almost any speed could be reached if the trains are run in tunnels evacuated of air to reduce friction.

For the magnetically levitated hovertrains of the future, a new type of electric motor may be used, the so-called linear motor which does not rotate. The linear electric motor is sometimes described as being like an ordinary rotating motor which has been sliced apart and stretched out along a line instead of having to rotate around a central axis. When electric currents pass through the motor, magnetic forces are created between the motor and a metal strip placed below it. These forces can be made to push the motor, and anything attached to it, along. In a conventional motor, the magnetic forces make the device rotate. Whereas this is ideal for powering wheels, the pure linear force of the linear motor is a great deal more useful when vehicles without wheels need to be driven along a track as in the overtrain principle. The very high speed hovertrains would have difficulty drawing electricity from an overhead pantograph. Accordingly, the latest idea is to make the track form the motor, carrying the electric currents, leaving the train merely to 'surf' along what amounts to a magnetic wave generated by the track.

Surprisingly, the future may herald a return to a new Steam Age on some railways. Whereas oil supplies appear to be very limited, coal promises to be abundant for hundreds of years to come. However, as well as coal, there may be large quantities of the low grade oil called 'bunkering fuel' available. This is the residue left behind after the high grade fractions have been extracted in oil refineries. So, for perhaps a century or more, such fuels might form the basis of a new steam-powered economy for many applications. The steam engines of the

twenty-first century should be very different both in appearance and design, from those of the nineteenth and twentieth centuries. The traditional steam engine was designed with comparatively little regard for fuel economy, when coal was cheap and plentiful and there was no need to maximise fuel efficiency. Steam engines of the next century could potentially compete very effectively in terms of cost and performance with other sources of motive power as a consequence of detailed development to improve fuel burning and overall efficiency. Almost certainly, the boiler of a future steam engine would consist of a so-called 'fluidised bed' which could burn even the lowest grade fuels very efficiently and with little or no pollution. At Queen Mary College in London, a model of a steam locomotive using a 'fluidised bed' type boiler has been developed. The combustion of low grade bunkering fuel or powdered coal is combined with sand through which a current of air is continually blown, making it appear like a boiling liquid. This ensures highly efficient burning. To remove pollutants like sulphur, minerals such as lime can be added, so the boiler can be environmentally as well as economically satisfactory. The design also incorporates recycling of the pure water used to raise steam, thus cutting down on another major cost of the traditional steam locomotive: that of preparing a continuous supply of clean water. It should also be possible to raise steam in this new generation of steam locomotives as quickly as a present day diesel engine takes to reach normal operating power. In countries where the highest speeds are not regarded as the utmost priority, entire rail networks could be operated on low quality fuels by using fluidised bed steam locomotives, although a more likely application of the fluidised bed boiler would be in using the low grade fuels in power stations to generate electricity for the fastest long distance electrically powered trains.

Above
The *Pendulum Train*, being developed by
Bliss Pendair Ltd. Because the cars are
suspended from an overhead monorail (by
magnetic levitation) the train can swing
outwards at corners, thus providing a
comfortable ride at fairly high speeds
without resisting powerful lateral forces,
such as those created by high winds.

Right
British Rail's *Hovercraft* provides a fast,
comfortable journey over the English
Channel. Elevated by powerful downwards-
pointing fans, the hovercraft can travel at
speeds of 100 km (60 mi) per hour or more
because of the reduced surface contact and
thereby reduced friction.

Opposite top and bottom
Design for a *magnetically-levitated vehicle*
being developed by Professor Rhodes at
Warwick University in England.

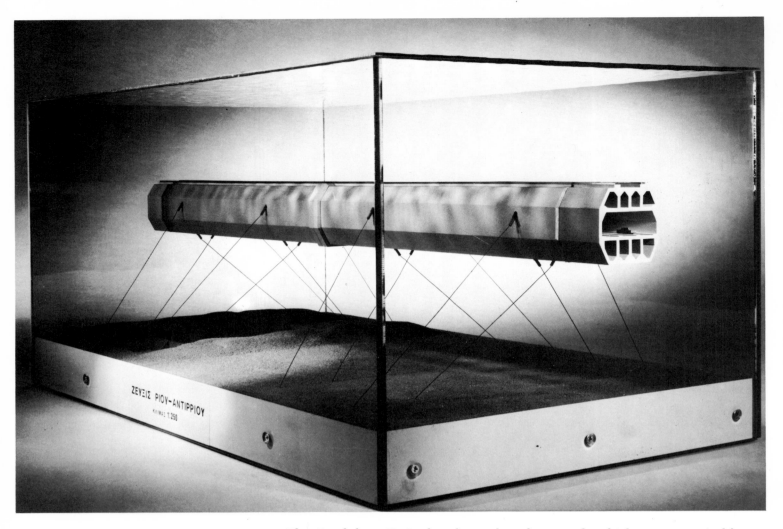

Above

Archimedean (Buoyant submerged tube) bridge. A 2,500 m (8,250 ft) buoyant, concrete traffic tunnel, floating 20 m (66 ft) below the water surface, and anchored to the sea bed at a maximum depth of 70 m (231 ft) by steel cables, has been designed by Submerged Buoyant Structures Limited as a proposed link between the cities of Rion and Andirrion in Greece. The tunnel would be able to accommodate three lanes of road traffic as well as two railway tracks in each direction and would be fully ventilated by a forced draught. When necessary, an additional traffic tube could be added on top of the existing tube to cope with increased traffic.

Opposite

Boeing's 27.4 m (90 ft) 250 passenger *jetfoil* can cruise in 3.7 m (12 ft) waves at 45 knots (83.3 km/h or 51.8 mph) while giving its passengers a smooth ride by means of its fully submerged foils, jet propulsion system, and automatically controlled stabilizers. The propulsion system's jet engine uses water instead of air. The craft's Automatic Control System (ACS) combines weather information and the skipper's decisions on speed and direction with the computer's speed and accuracy to provide the jetfoil's almost unequalled stability.

The Pendulum Train has been designed for urban use where ground space is too valuable to be made available for railways. It consists of passenger cars which are suspended from an overhead monorail and can thus swing outwards at corners to produce a comfortable ride at fairly high speeds without generating powerful sideways forces which would otherwise cause discomfort to the passengers. The suspension unit uses magnetic levitation at the monorail track. Because very high speeds are not necessary, conventional electric motors are used for propulsion instead of the more experimental linear motor which is mainly beneficial at high speeds where the reduced friction cuts down energy losses.

Many countries, however, would still not be able to fulfill their transportation needs purely by road or rail, especially where large areas of water may have to be crossed. Whereas aircraft offer a convenient form of travel, regardless of land formations and seas, it may always be less costly to make journeys by surface routes. So there are strong incentives for developing ways of crossing water quickly and efficiently. Although tunnels and bridges can be built in some places, it will never be possible to build such road and rail links in all places where connections are needed. One solution is to expand greatly the use of

hovercraft, which are economical but at the same time quite fast. The hovercraft is elevated by means of powerful downwards-pointing fans which produce a cushion of air between itself and water, or indeed any flat surface. By reducing the surface contact, it avoids wasting energy in the way that ships do when they produce a bow-wave. Speeds of 100 kilometres per hour and even more are possible because the only friction to be overcome is from the air. At the same time, the hovercraft is not truly an aircraft because the lifting action depends on the presence of a flat surface below. But this makes it possible to lift the craft with only a fraction of the effort required to fly a helicopter or an airliner. The hovercraft thus provides a useful compromise between saving energy and maintaining fairly high speeds. Although one of the wonders of twentieth century engineering, the hovercraft remains relatively little used even after two decades of development. It has suffered from very strong competition from existing transport systems determined to maintain their share of the market, but the speed advantage which it has over shipping, and its low cost compared with air travel should eventually win hovercraft a permanent place in future transportation policies all over the world.

In spite of vastly improved methods of surface transport, the average person of

the early twenty-first century will probably be even more familiar with air transport than we are today. One reason is that the closing decades of the twentieth century may well witness an unprecedented glut of oil: continuing over-production throughout the world, belying the austerity to come in the years of oil scarcity which should begin during the twenty-first century. Thus, even though aircraft are large consumers of fuel, the world may possess a comprehensive network of air services accessible almost to anybody. The aircraft industry, however, is not likely to be taken by surprise when the oil shortage begins. By

the turn of the century, some radically new types of aircraft should be available, and a good many more should be on the drawing boards – all designed to keep up the volume of air traffic in spite of the coming oil shortage.

Nuclear power is already emerging as the most economical form of energy for industrial and domestic use, cheaper than oil or coal power. Small reactors can, in principle, be used to power turbines for aircraft propulsion, and may become economically worthwhile on very large aircraft. The power unit would need to be contained within a crash-resistant vessel which, even in the event of being

fractured, would be designed to produce rapid cooling of the nuclear core with minimal leakage of radiation. It may well be argued that a single nuclear bomb tested in the atmosphere poses a far greater threat to human health than hundreds of aircraft flying around the world powered by nuclear reactors. In spite of this, the debate about the environmental consequences of nuclear powered aircraft, is likely to be every bit as fierce as debates during the twentieth century concerning such issues as nuclear fuel re-processing and the storage of nuclear wastes. But economic needs may well win out in the end. Indeed, it is

known that air forces of the world have been considering the use of nuclear powered aircraft for some time, and even by the year 2000, if they are made, most of these aircraft will probably be for military use. Freedom from having to land and re-fuel will be an important strategic advantage. As the coming oil shortage begins to bite, however, passenger fleets throughout the world may also be converted to nuclear power.

Hydrogen is another alternative source of power for both jet and piston engines on aircraft not big enough to house nuclear reactors. Because hydrogen can be produced by the action of electricity on water, hydrogen fuel could be readily available, albeit rather more expensive than present-day oil-based fuels, for as long as the world is capable of generating electricity. However, hydrogen has to be stored at temperatures low enough to keep it liquid and occupies rather more space than either gasoline or kerosene. Therefore, hydrogen-powered aircraft would probably need large tanks fixed on to the wings, but other than that, their appearance might be little different from present-day aircraft.

Although supersonic jets may never account for the largest proportion of air traffic, it is possible that a complete global network of frequent supersonic flights may exist by the turn of the century. The Anglo–French Concord and the Soviet Tupulev 144 supersonic airliners have not yet benefitted from the economic advantages of mass-production and worldwide demand. However, if the current oil glut continues, together with the affluence it can produce, there may be a place for large numbers of such aircraft in the years to come. The only potentially limiting factor might be the supply of oil. But, even if supersonic transports are forced to rely on hydrogen fuel when oil is no longer available, there could still be a healthy demand for supersonic travel among the business community.

Noise pollution is another area in which the future offers huge scope for improvement. In the past, machinery was developed with little regard for noise production, but the recent opposition to projects such as the Concorde has shown that to neglect the aspect of noise pollution can cause huge economic losses. The result is that a new generation of much quieter jet engines has already been developed for aircraft, and in the future noise levels should be reduced still further.

Whereas much of the current effort aimed at reducing aircraft noise is concerned with the turbo jet, noise from propeller driven aircraft can also be reduced. The so-called 'ducted pro-

Above
The *U.S. Space Shuttle*, which will make weekly space flights from the 1980s on, being transported to its base by a Boeing 747.

Opposite
The Anglo-French *Concorde* supersonic airliner.

An Islander aircraft mounted with *Dowty Ducted Propulsors*, cylindrical ducts which enclose the engine and propellor and thereby contain most of the aircraft's noise. The two engines on this Islander craft were lowered 37.5 (15 in) below the standard position to bring the fan efflux completely below the wing surface and provide a smooth flight.

pulsor' achieves this by enclosing the engine and propeller within a cylindrical duct which stops most of the noise from getting out. Thus, super-quiet jets and vertical and short take off aircraft for businessmen, could be far more common.

But in situations where noise cannot be eliminated at source, a further novel development is showing promise. Scientists in a number of centres are developing a technique sometimes called 'anti-sound'. In effect, this is a sound which cancells another sound. It is still a far cry from generating 'beams of silence' to quieten passing aircraft or trains, but progress is being made. Sound, including noise, consists basically of a series of compressions and rarifications in the air. A sound wave created by a noisy object, travels out to the human ear as successive layers of air, alternate regions being of compressed and stretched air. The anti-sound concept suggests that another sound wave be super-imposed onto the first, so that the regions of stretched air have compressed air super-imposed upon them while the compressed regions of air receive a force which rarifies the air in those positions. Thus, the 'bumpy air' produced by noise would become 'smoothed out' again by means of the extra sound wave. This is very difficult to do in practical situations, but Dr

Malcom Swinbanks of Cambridge University has already been able to reduce the noise from an air conditioner. At the Institute of Sound and Vibration Research at Southampton University in England, scientists working on the problem of noise for pilots of high-performance jet aircraft, have developed a system using a tiny microphone in the pilot's headset. This picks up the jet noise the pilot would normally hear and super-imposes it, after a small time delay, onto the sounds going into his ear. The thin and the thick regions of air in the two sources of sound then cancel out each other with the effect that jet noise is considerably reduced.

Long range aircraft designs of the year 2000 may also vary little from today's. The majority of aircraft could still be sub-sonic, providing mass transportation at the lowest possible cost rather than giving supersonic travel to all. However, future aircraft design may diversify to meet a wider range of market needs. One case in point is the aircraft with X-shaped wings, currently being designed experimentally by the Lockheed Aircraft Company, which is derived from the conventional helicopter which is limited to speeds of around 300 kilometres per hour because of the resistance to forward motion caused by having

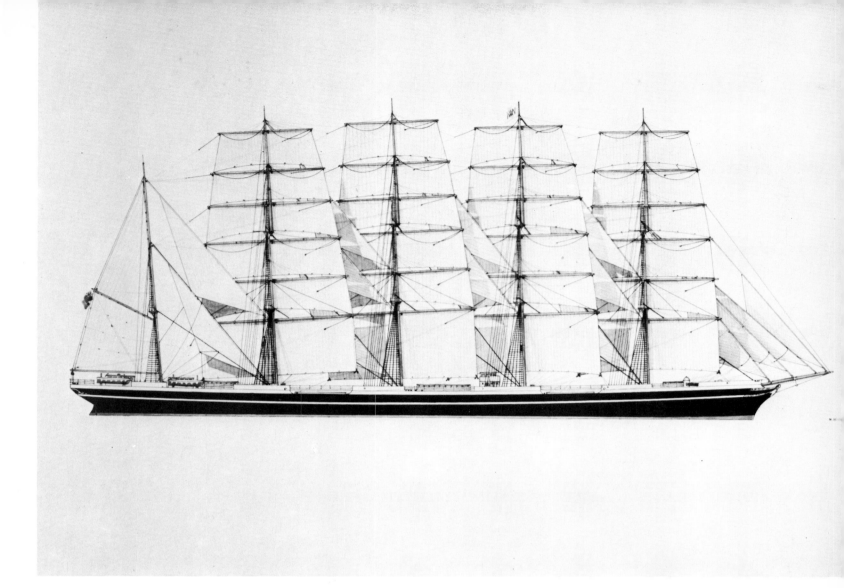

the rotor in motion. Because an aircraft with X-shaped wings is able to stop its rotors altogether and trim them for optimum lift with minimum drag, cruising speeds can be reached which are comparable to those of any other jet aircraft. By rotating the four wings, like the rotor blades of a helicopter, the aircraft can take off vertically. When in forward flight, the rotor speed is gradually reduced until a forward speed is reached at which the rotors can be stopped altogether and provide lift like two pairs of ordinary wings – a forward-pointing pair and a swept-back pair.

For long distance travel where time-saving is of utmost importance, the future businessman may be able to fly sub-orbitally, reaching any part of the world in less than an hour, because of research going into the American Space Shuttle, which should be making weekly space flights during the 1980s. Based on the Space Shuttle concept, the sub-orbital airliner would be capable of taking off from the ground and landing like an airliner, but also capable of being boosted out into space by rocket motors, reaching speeds of around 30,000 kilometres per hour. This is nearly fast enough to go permanently into orbit, but the sub-orbital airliner would spend most of the flight-time in space and would need to be

able to withstand the heat and stresses of re-entering the atmosphere at the end of the journey just like any other spacecraft. It would represent the ultimate in high-speed air travel. Any craft travelling faster would be flung out to space by the force of its own motion.

On a more mundane but practical level, it is possible to anticipate the return of another form of air travel: the airship. In their heyday, airships were magnificent and highly efficient machines, capable of transporting big payloads over long distances without using large amounts of fuel. By the beginning of the next century, airships may already be back in service as an economical means of freight transport supplement the work of shipping. The disasters which overcame some of the early airships were caused in some instances by the use of inflammable hydrogen gas for providing the lift, and in others by inadequate engineering design. Since that time, however, helium has been introduced instead of hydrogen for both airships and balloons, and the design requirements for the safe operation of airships are more fully understood. Airship enthusiasts point out that there is no longer any reason to discount the airship on grounds of safely. With this in mind, there have already been

Windrose Ship's *five-masted square-rigged barque*. Recent studies have shown that for freight transport, sailing ships could be superior to motor ships as far as construction and operation costs, ship manning requirements, and cargo capacity. Among recent designs from England, Germany and the U.S., are proposals for modifications which can be made to existing ships.

suggestions from the Soviet Union of using airships to tow long 'trains' of balloons carrying cargoes such as oil as an alternative to using tankers and pipelines. A further advantage of the airship has been put forward by Dr Gabriel Khoury, a Jordanian engineer working at London University's Imperial College, who has drawn up plans for an airship covered with solar cells: devices which convert sunlight into electricity. These 'sun-ships' could be powered entirely by the electricity they generate from the Sun's rays. Because of the airship's size, it lends itself very well to being covered with solar cells. Each cell produces a small quantity of electric current, but collectively, the sun-ship's cells can generate enough to propel the craft at 100 kilometres an hour or even more by means of electric motors connected to airscrew blades.

Equally, with the ever increasing environmental consciousness of the world, the Age of Sail could be revived on a more sophisticated level. One indication of this trend is the five-master barque designed by Mike Willoughby, who runs a ship yard in Southern England. Based on traditional sailing ship design, Willoughby's ship, which is designed to use

twin 1,250 brake horse-power diesel motors to propel the ship when it is becalmed at sea, hydraulic winches to take the strain out of hoisting and trimming the sails, and the best radar and radio navigation equipment currently available, is designed to be a 12,000 ton container vessel. It could cruise at a steady $12\frac{1}{2}$ knots on transatlantic routes under most conditions. The relatively slower speeds of such sailing ships would be no great disadvantage for the purpose of transporting most bulk cargoes, and the use of containers and modern equipment would eliminate the chores associated with the operating of old fashioned sailing vessels.

The changing pattern of world energy sources at the beginning of the twenty-first century should also be reflected in ship-building trends. As with steam trains, cheap supplies of coal and bunkering fuel may be used to power a significant proportion of world shipping, with ships powered by highly efficient steam boilers having fluidised bed furnaces. And, as with air transport, a growth of nuclear-power for ships can also be anticipated, with a dwindling proportion of ships running on conventional fuel oil. After more than

With the replacement of the disastrous hydrogen of the past by safe helium gas, airships may be widely used for freight transport. The Soviet Union has suggested using airships to tow long 'trains' of balloons carrying cargoes such as oil as an alternative to tankers and pipelines.

It is also likely that airships will be powered by solar energy. Dr. Gabriel Khoury, a Jordanian engineer working at London University's Imperial College, has drawn up plans for an airship covered with solar cells. This would generate enough power to propell the ship at 100 km (60 mi) per hour or more.

twenty years of development, nuclear reactors for ships and submarines now appear to pose no greater threat to the environment than nuclear power stations on land. In spite of this, there are still only a handful of military and non-military nuclear-powered vessels: The Russian ice-breakers *Lenin*, *Artika* and *Siberia*, the Japanese cargo ship N. S. *Mutsu*, and the German cargo ship N. S. *Otto Hahn*. The slow growth of civil nuclear ships may continue, but the recession in the shipping industry, which took place during the 1970s, has put a damper on most new ship-building projects.

The biggest overall improvement in commercial shipping to take place by the year 2000 will be the reduction of accidents and sinkings. Currently, more than a thousand of the world's fleet of some seven thousand tankers can be expected to meet with an accident each year, forty of them, on average, sinking. Many of these incidents are traceable to human error. The application of

computer control for ships, linked with obstacle sensing devices such as radar and sonar, promises to improve the safety of large ships very significantly. Satellite tracking of ships, linked to centrally co-ordinated traffic control, can also substantially reduce the toll of lost vessels. The remaining factor is the weather. Here again, however, satellite surveillance offers to reduce the problem of uncertainties by transmitting weather forecasts continually to the ship's on-board computer which can then take action automatically, or warn the captain of any approaching problem. The ultimate answer, however, may be to send most freight by nuclear submarine. The necessary technology to do this should be fully established by the turn of the century, and thus, by eliminating weather problems, accidents and sinkings may become a thing of the past.

Nuclear submarine. Because of the rising cost of fossil fuels, nuclear energy may well become a more widely-used power source for military and commercial vessels.

Space: The New Frontier

The human race may be destined to live in space, and a mass migration into space may take place a great deal sooner than we expect. From the science of biology we learn that life forms of all kinds grow and flourish in every suitable habitat made available to them, and there now seems to be no substantial reason why humans should not be able to live adequately in space and on other planets.

Space technology now appears to have reached a threshold from which huge steps forward can be made in the closing decades of this century. The rate of progress is illustrated by the history of the world space effort to date. In the 1960s and early 1970s, it was not technically or economically feasible for man to perform large-scale engineering tasks in space. In spite of this, however, the spirit of competition between the United States and the Soviet Union gave rise to a 'space race' which resulted in a series of manned space landings on the Moon. The cost of the Apollo series of Moon landings was enormous, and may be judged to have been premature in the light of present-day developments which suggest that future flights to the Moon could be achieved at a tiny fraction of the cost of the Apollo series, and with fewer attendant dangers. One of the initial aims of the American Space Shuttle project is to reduce, by a large factor, the cost of putting payloads into orbit. As such, the Shuttle, which is the first re-usable space craft, represents the threshold of technical achievement which will make possible ever more complex, large-scale engineering in space.

The Space Shuttle takes off from Earth like a rocket, using a rocket motor-back-pack which is later jettisoned, and lands again on Earth like an aircraft. It can transport not only its own crew, but also passengers, and has a huge cargo-hold capable of carrying large satellites or a space laboratory from which scientific research can be conducted. Before the Space Shuttle was created, it was necessary to plan space exploration years ahead of any launch. However, for the rest of the century, it should be possible to make space flights as a matter of routine. The Shuttle can ferry men into orbit and back down to Earth again as and when necessary, and it should be able to make space flights every week or so throughout the 1980s. Any scientist or engineer (or military expert) needing to travel into orbit would simply take the next shuttle flight, stay as long as necessary, and then return at his convenience.

It is difficult to imagine even a small proportion of the immense opportunities this new facility holds out. One of the great advantages of having a re-usable space vehicle is that it can ferry-up one payload after another into orbit. Very large orbiting stations could not be launched in their complete form directly from Earth because sufficiently large rockets have not been developed, and the cost of developing such enormous rockets would probably be prohibitive, but huge space stations could be built in kit form, one module being joined to the next in orbit. The Space Shuttle is likely to be used as a general 'work-horse' for the rest of this century, and the assembly of modular constructions in orbit should become commonplace, especially since there are many advantages to constructing in space rather than on the Earth's surface. The lack of gravity reduces the problems of structural stresses and strains – thus space stations and other constructions do not have to be given the strength to support their own weight – and, furthermore, space is a clean, pollution-free environment in which construction techniques such as welding can be conducted in ideal conditions.

Once these huge orbiting space stations are completed, they are likely to become the platforms from which hundreds of robot space probes could be launched cheaply and easily to further the exploration of the solar system, improve the relaying of detailed television pictures and scientific observations of the planets and their moons back to Earth, and mount lunar and asteroidal mining operations. The technology needed is already developed and available, and the commercial and military pressures to develop space technology are likely to ensure that governments will

Opposite top
Artist's impression of a *Space Shuttle* with long manipulator arms, retrieving a satellite in low earth orbit for return to earth and refurbishment.

Opposite bottom
Artist's impression of the strap-on solid fuel rockets separating from the *Space Shuttle* two minutes after take-off. These rockets will augment the shuttle's three main rocket engines which burn liquid oxygen and liquid hydrogen carried in the large tank under the shuttle. The two spent solid rockets will fall back into the Atlantic Ocean and be towed to the Kennedy Space Centre for cleaning, refurbishment, and reuse in subsequent shuttle missions. The only part of the shuttle system that is not re-useable is the liquid propellant tank. This will be released eight minutes after take-off and is burnt up as it re-enters the atmosphere.

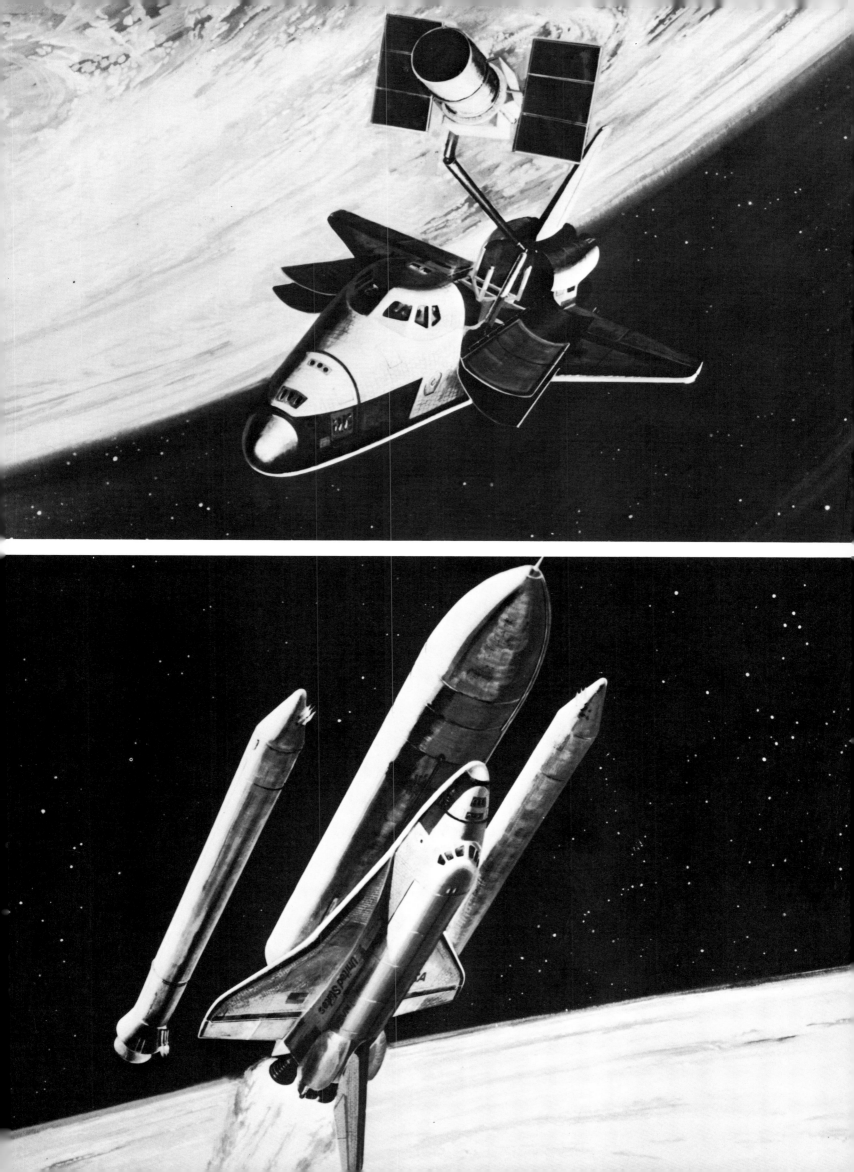

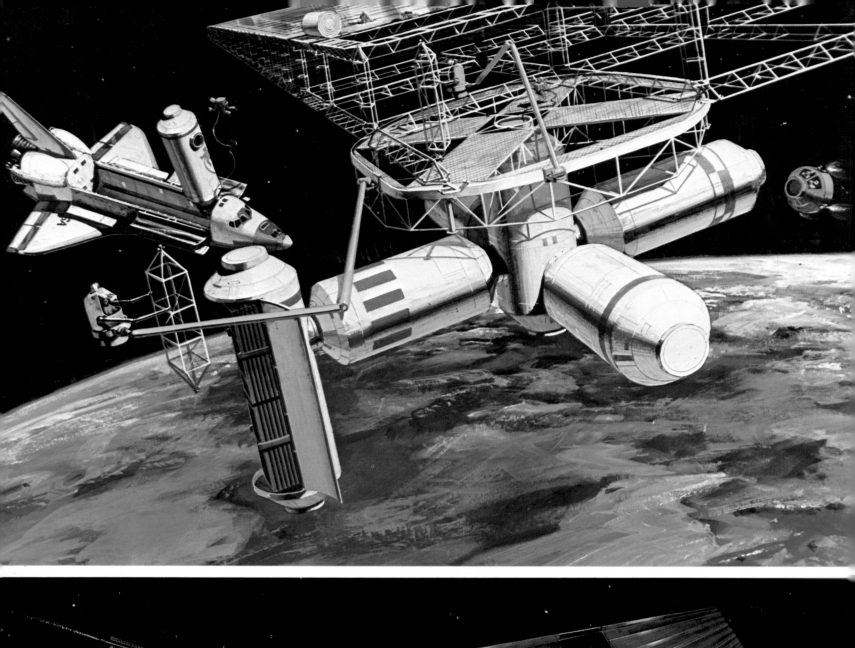

Opposite top
Artist's impression of an economical modular *Space Station*. This part of the Space Shuttle programme will use the Shuttle Orbiter as its method of transportation. Accommodating up to twelve scientists and crewmen, the station consists of five basic elements: the airlock module, the manipulator module, the central assembly module, an electric power boom, and a basic structural module.

Opposite bottom
Massive *satellite solar power stations*, such as this one nearing completion, could provide the Earth with an abundant supply of energy. Each satellite, carrying large collector arrays of solar cells would be placed in synchronous orbit around the Earth. It would beam microwave energy to a 52 sq. km (20 sq. mi) receiving antenna on the Earth which would convert the energy to electricity. One such satellite could deliver the equivalent of the power output of several nuclear power plants.

Above right
The launch configuration of the *Space Shuttle* just after take-off. The combined thrust of the shuttle and its strap-on boosters is 2,891,250 kg (6,425,000 lb), almost the thrust developed by the Saturn V or Apollo vehicles.

Right
Spacelab, a combined NASA and ESA (European Space Agency) project, is an orbital facility which will provide a pressurised laboratory (the centre module) and/or an unpressurised platform to conduct basic or applied research tasks in the unique environment of Space. Spacelab is a reusable system which will be transported to and from orbit in the cargo bay of the Space Shuttle Orbiter. The Orbiter and laboratory are linked by a tunnel, enabling scientists to spend their off duty time in the Orbiter's cabin.

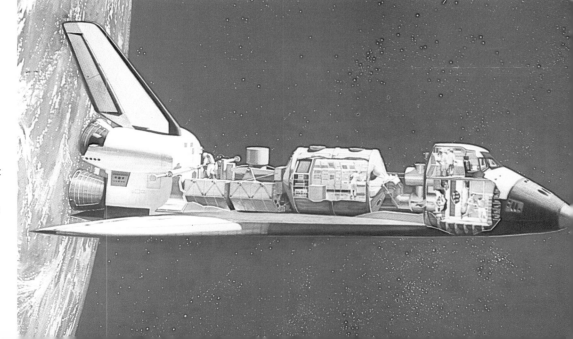

Left
This cutaway of an *orbital laboratory* shows the various elements needed to sustain human habitation: a gym; a cinema; washing facilties; and dining and leisure rooms.

Below
A *mining operation in the Asteroid Belt*, the workforce of which would be housed in the space colonies. The minerals from these operations would be used for building the space stations, and supplying the colonies' manufacturing industries.

be increasingly willing to commit themselves to extensive programmes of space engineering, exploration, and research. In addition, space could be exploited for providing solar power: by means of satellites carrying huge collecting mirrors, arrays of solar cells, which would capture the Sun's energy and generate electricity for the energy-hungry decades ahead. Manufacturing industries, which can benefit from conditions of zero gravity, could be set up, and the scientific community could use space as the ideal environment for scientific research. Astronomy would benefit enormously by being conducted from above the Earth's atmosphere which reduces the efficiency of Earth-based telescopes and makes certain studies, such as X-ray astronomy, impossible from the surface of the Earth.

The space effort is no longer confined to competition between the Russians and the Americans however. Most other countries now wish to have a stake in space development. The European Space Agency (ESA) is now concerned with a major part of the Space Shuttle programme. ESA is to build the space laboratory which will be carried into orbit by the Shuttle for conducting scientific experiments of a degree of complexity and thoroughness never

before possible in space. The whole world is now geared towards the conquest of space, the outcome of which could soon be human exploration of most of the planets and other bodies within our solar system.

One of the principal expenses of all current space launches is the cost of fuel. However, the Moon's gravity is only about one sixth of earth's gravity, so very much less fuel is required to launch vehicles into space from the Moon than from Earth. Permanent Moon bases would therefore facilitate the launching of construction materials into space much more cheaply than from Earth. A further advantage is that the Moon possesses no atmosphere, making space launches a great deal simpler and less hazardous than on Earth.

Space vehicles launched from the Moon would not have to withstand the frictional heating which affects spacecraft flying through the Earth's thick atmosphere, thus enabling novel methods of launching, such as the lunar 'sling-shot' launcher to be used. The hovertrain principle of magnetic levitation could be applied to construct these 'sling-shot' launchers, which consist of a metal track, several kilometres long, that incorporates a motor. The spacecraft would hover magnetically above the

A mock up of the interior of *Spacelab* at ESTEL, Noordwijk, Holland, showing the experiment racks and consoles. The Spacelab-missions will carry out experiments involving materials processing, life sciences, pharmaceutical manufacturing biological and zoological processes in Space, in addition to earth and astronomical viewing.

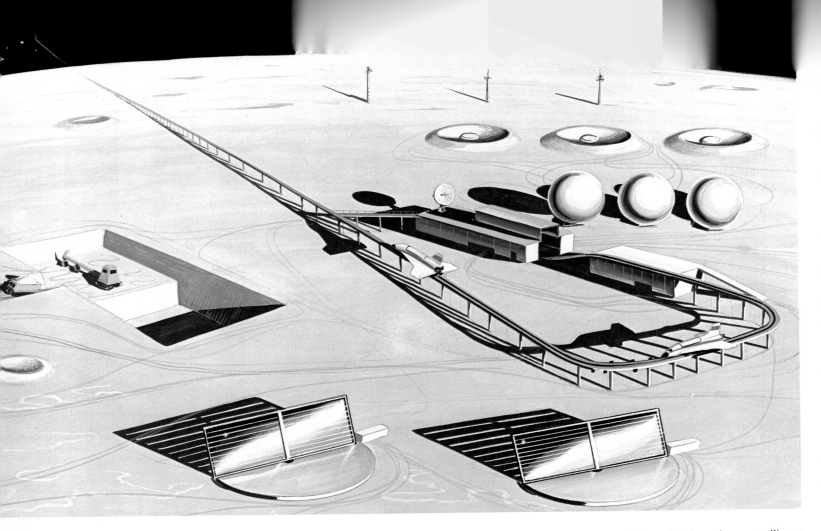

track and be propelled like a surf-board riding on the magnetic wave induced electrically in the track. This would sufficiently accelerate the spacecraft to allow it to take off and achieve the Moon's escape velocity. On-board rocket motors would then be necessary for only steering and maneouvering in space. This development and others which take advantage of the Moon's unique environment could reduce the cost of space exploration by yet another big factor.

Apart from the Space Shuttle, there will also be space ships that remain in space, not landing on any planet. These might very well be powered by nuclear rocket motors. Nuclear reactors for space application, which have been under study for many years in the United States, can be used to heat hydrogen gas and expel it at very high temperatures and pressures as in an ordinary rocket motor. They should have a much higher power-to-weight ratio than ordinary rockets. Some of the hydrogen gas expelled from the exhaust would be converted into radio-active tritium, an isotope of hydrogen. On Earth, this would pollute the environment, but out in space, the relatively small quantities of tritium produced would pose only a minor radiation hazard. Also, the consequences of a collision, and possible radiation leakage, would be less serious in space than in a planetary environment. Therefore, nuclear propulsion could become a safe and cheap means of propelling deep

space probes, as manned exploration of the solar system proceeds.

While large-scale, manned space exploration of the Solar System gets under way, robot probes could also be deployed for exploring the stars. At first consideration, this may seem to be a very difficult project to attempt because the nearest star is no less than four light years away, meaning that even if a spacecraft were able to travel at the immense speed of light (300,000 kilometres per second) it would take four years to reach the nearest star. Nevertheless, a star probe has already been designed. It is the end result of a study involving thirteen scientists at the British Interplanetary Society, the organisation which, before the Second World War, described how manned landings on the Moon could be achieved, and predicted communications satellites long before space flight was proved possible. Daedalus, the name given to the space probe, would weigh 50,000 tonnes, be constructed in space, and be powered by nuclear fusion. There would be a succession of tiny hydrogen bomb explosions in its combustion chamber which would accelerate it to more than one-tenth the speed of light. The British Interplanetary Society team suggests it should be used to probe Barnard's Star, which is about six light years away and is known to have planets in orbit around it. It could thus be a place where another civilisation might live. Daedalus would take about fifty years to

Lunar base. Sling shot launcher propelling a shuttle spaceward with construction materials for a space colony. Mechanical excavators collect material for the power convertor of the sling shot launcher. Solar power panels provide electricity for the living quarters of the mining community.

reach Barnard's Star, and on arrival would automatically deploy smaller probes to investigate the planets. These would transmit information back to the mother ship which, in turn, would relay it to Earth.

Although commercial incentives for developing a starship may not be very strong, even by the year 2000, there may be other pressures which could encourage the development of a starship. Firstly, the world could afford to build one by then, and secondly, the need for a means of escaping from our solar system at some time in the future may be foreseen as necessary. Escape could be essential as a result of war or a natural catastrophe such as the approach of a cloud of space dust and gas which could envelope our solar system (causing drastic climatic changes on Earth as well as reducing solar radiation throughout our solar system), or such as the approach of black holes – massive collapsed stars which have already been discovered at great distances from Earth. These are completely black because their gravity is so strong that no radiation, including light, can escape into the universe outside the hole. They are thought to travel through space like huge vacuum cleaners, consuming all solid objects in their paths. Any star, planet, or other object in Space is attracted to the hole by gravity, and once trapped within a certain distance can never escape. The approach of a black hole, however, can

be detected. Some of the first effects on Earth would be changes in the tidal patterns of the oceans. Abnormally high or abnormally low tides could precede the arrival of a black hole. As it approaches, the tidal disturbances would become large, and climatic changes would sweep the planet. Future inhabitants of Earth, however, would be able to escape in starships, provided they made the decision to leave soon enough, before the gravitational pull became too strong. Paradoxically, they may even use black holes as a means of starship propulsion, for it is calculated that miniature black holes could be contained by magnetism within a reaction chamber, and manipulated by man to convert mass into energy, and thus provide the most powerful source of energy ever to be tapped artificially.

If black holes are invisible, how can we be sure that they exist? Until very recently, astonomers strongly believed that black holes existed but had no actual proof. However, in 1978, proof was forthcoming in the form of observations of both X-rays and ultraviolet light from a very unusual star called Cygnus X–1. Before 1978, astronomers detecting X-rays from the star by using X-ray telescopes mounted on satellites orbiting above the Earth's atmosphere, had concluded that the X-rays were so powerful that they could only be produced by the inflow of hot gases into a callapsed star. But the star could have been a dwarf star

Artist's impression of how a *black hole* attracts matter. The gravitational field of the black hole distorts the supergiant star out of spherical shape and drags material from it.

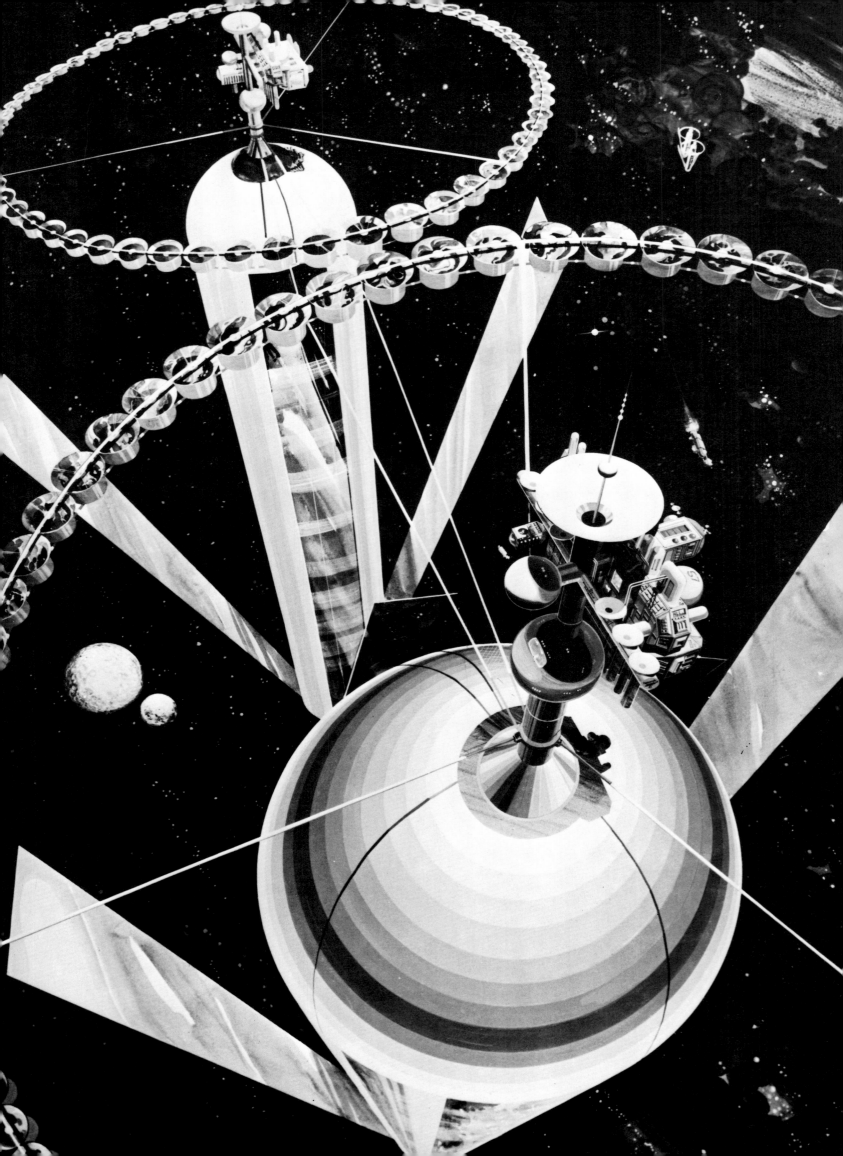

(an ordinary sized star at the end of its life), or one of the so-called neutron stars produced by a stellar explosion, or a black hole. The only way of distinguishing between these three possibilities was to measure the mass of the collapsed star. Cygnus X–1 was already known to be a double star, because a visible star was observed to be moving in orbit around a dark companion. It was the dark sister star which was thought to be the black hole. In 1978, astronomers from Princeton University in the United States, and from University College and the Appleton Laboratory in England, finally established the mass of the dark companion by measuring its orbital speed of flight around the ordinary bright star. This was done by observing the effect of the orbital rotation upon ultraviolet light being radiated by Cygnus X–1. The ultraviolet light frequency was altered to such an extent that the astronomers were able to calculate the mass of the dark star as being at least five times the mass of the Sun. According to the equations of Albert Einstein's theory of relativity, a collapsed star of such a mass could only be a black hole, and not a neutron star nor even a dwarf star. In the future, the presence of black holes will continue to be inferred from circumstantial evidence like this, and, as far as it is known at present, no black holes are likely to reach Earth in the foreseeable future.

Planets in our own solar system could be exploited long before star flights are undertaken. At present, both the United States and the Soviet Union have launched robot space probes to investigate conditions on neighbouring planets. The Soviet Union has conducted a long term programme of research into space engineering and scientific tests using the Soyuz space capsules and the Salyut orbiting space station. They have also set world records for the length of time humans have spent continuously in space. The Russians probably have more knowledge than anybody about the medical effects of long term weightlessness. If their programme of lengthy space flights continues, Russian cosmonauts should within a few years be prepared for flights to Mars which may take many months, or even years, to complete.

The next concrete step in this direction could be the setting up of completely artificially constructed space colonies. According to a growing body of expert opinion, it is already technically feasible to construct a pioneering space colony which would be self-sufficient, and also allow its inhabitants to conduct further space engineering projects and build more colonies as they are needed. In 1974, an American scientist, Gerard O'Neill of Princeton University, announced in the pages of the scientific journal *Nature* that viable space colonies could be set up well before the turn of the century. As the basis for his calculations, he assumed that a budget equal to the American expenditure on the Apollo series of Moon flights could be made available, and he worked out whether present-day technology could provide an adequate, habitable space station that could be self-sufficient. O'Neill designed a pioneering colony capable of supporting ten thousand humans, and he calculated that this could be constructed before the end of the century without exceeding the assumed budget. All of the technical requirements for such a colony – computers, rocket motors, the Space Shuttle for transportation to and from Earth, solar energy devices, and so on – would all be available. On the basis of his caculations, it seems that whenever the political decision to build such a colony is made, the technical means to construct it will be available. Recognising that the World

Above
The *Torus Space Colony*, designed by NASA, consists of a large wheel with an outer 'tire', composed of cinder-like lunar material, for shielding radiation. The central hub contains the docking station and communications antenna. Six spokes connect the hub with the outer wheel and provide entry and exit to living and agricultural areas. The burnished disc floating above the wheel is a mirror that reflects sunlight onto slanted panels and into chevron shields that screen out cosmic rays.

Opposite
Artist's impression of a 32 km (19 mi) long and 6½ km (4 mi) wide *Cylindrical Space Settlement* in orbit between the Earth and the Moon. The cylinder, which rotates to create an Earth-like gravity, would contain an Earth-like landscape capable of supporting a population of up to two or three million. The teacup-shaped containers ringing the cylinder are agricultural stations. The cylinder is capped by a manufacturing and power station. Large moveable rectangular mirrors on the sides of the cylinders, hinged at the lower end, would direct sunlight into the interior, regulate the seasons, and control the day-night cycle.

Opposite top
Interior of one of the large *Cylindrical Space Colonies* showing the vast parks and lakes capable of being built within the cylinder's enormous 'land' area (hundreds of square kilometres/miles).

Opposite bottom
The ability to build and mould the landscape inside the colony allows the colonist to construct replicas of their Earth home. In this case, it is *San Francisco*.

Above
Section through a *Torus Space Colony*. Any type of Earth-like landscape or climate would be possible to manufacture inside the colony: rural Oxfordshire, the Rocky Mountains, or the Amazon forest. A space colony of this size, constructed of materials from the moon or Asteroid Belt and manufactured in space, could support a population of two hundred thousand to several million. Inside Torus, the largest of four colonies proposed by Dr O'Neill of Princeton University, the Earth-like gravity would be produced by the rotation of the large cylinder every 114 seconds. In order to produce days, nights, and seasons, sunlight coming through the glass 'windows' would be controlled by mirrors outside.

A segment of a *Torus Space Colony* under final construction. The chevron shields, shown being installed, would absorb cosmic radiation while allowing sunlight to be reflected inside.

population is growing very rapidly, Gerard O'Neill calculated whether such space colonies could help allieviate problems of over-population on Earth. He decided that new colonies providing new living accommodation could be set up as fast as the growing human population required them.

The pioneering space colony, which Dr O'Neill believes could be with us whenever a decision is made to build it, would need to be constructed from materials shipped up from Earth using the Space Shuttle. The Shuttle would have to be modified to some extent to fly farther into space than is currently anticipated, for the colonies would not be placed in orbit around the Earth. They may instead be sited at one of the so-called Lagrangian Points, though this has not yet been decided. The advantage of a Lagrangian Point is that it is a gravita-

tionally stable point between the Earth and the Moon. Lagrangian Points are not on the straight line joining the Earth and the Moon, but are positioned some way off, where the combined gravities of the Earth and the Moon form what amounts to a gravitational hollow. Material objects tend to stay trapped in such positions, making them ideal for locating colonies which need to maintain communications with Earth, and probably with the Moon.

According to Dr O'Neill, subsequent space colonies, which could house perhaps ten million people each, could be constructed by the pioneering space colonists during the early part of the twenty-first century. These would not be made from Earth materials but would derive their raw materials from the Moon. Mining operations would need to have begun on the Moon to achieve this, and at present, this looks easily possible as an extension to American and Russian orbital space flights, already in progress. Building materials could be shot into space from the Moon in capsules, which would either be rocket-propelled or acelerated by devices such as the lunar 'sling-shot' launcher which would literally throw them up to the appropriate Lagrangian Point, or wherever else the colony is sited.

These ideas may seem like science fiction to many people, but they are founded firmly on scientific fact, and the American National Aeronautics and Space Administration's Ames Research Centre in California is already conducting a feasibility study of the O'Neill and other space colony designs. Dr O'Neill's space colonies, if they are built, will be truly magnificent structures: huge cylinders of metal and glass shimmering in the stark sunlight of empty space. The full-scale colonies would consist of hollow cylinders over thirty kilometres long and nearly seven kilometres wide. Inhabitants would live on the inner surface, and the cylinders would rotate once every two minutes to provide artificial gravity. The environment of the inner surfaces of such cylinders would be designed to resemble conditions on Earth as closely as possible: there could be water, trees, soil, plants, mountains, animals, and whatever else the colonists required. These colonies would derive all of their energy from the Sun. The walls of the colonies would consist of alternate strips of metal and glass, the metal wall forming the 'ground' in these simulated Earth conditions, the glass windows, stretching the entire length of the cylinders, forming the simulated 'sky'. The Sun would 'shine in' through the windows by being reflected from mirrors placed outside in space, and the rotating cylinders would need to be positioned end-on towards the Sun in order to catch the Sun's rays at all times. The mirrors outside the windows would also become shutters at night, closing over the windows to create darkness. To simulate winter and summer, the mirrors would be opened to different angles to increase or decrease the amount of solar radiation directed into the cylinder, and the length of the day could be adjusted according to the season if necessary. Another way in which solar energy could be harnessed is by means of huge, curved mirrors built out beyond the end of the cylinder furthest from the Sun. These would capture solar heat and concentrate it onto boilers in order to raise steam for electricity generation. An alternative, and more costly method of electricity generation, would be to use solar cells. Because converting the Sun's energy would be absolutely vital to the survival of such space colonies, it would be very important to keep the cylinders pointed accurately towards the Sun, and the simplest way to achieve this would be to link the cylinders together in pairs. Each cylinder would thus restrain its companion's tendency to spin away from correct alignment.

By the time such colonies have been built, it is likely that telecommunications will have advanced beyond almost anything we can imagine today. At the very least it should be possible for all colonists to have a cheap, or even free, telephone service linking them with Earth. Because of this, and the whole range of other facilities which could be provided by a new telecommunications system, the colonists should not feel any great sense of isolation from the mother planet. It should also not be too costly for colonists to visit Earth. In 1974, Gerard O'Neill calculated that it would cost only $3,000 on average to provide each colonist with his home in the sky, and to fly him there. With the development of re-usable spacecraft, it should soon be no more expensive to fly to a space colony from Earth than it is to take a long distance air flight at today's prices.

Transport systems within each space cylinder, and those from one cylinder to another could be quite different from future transport on Earth. For example, it would be a great advantage to use the outer surface of the cylinders to travel the longest distances in a colony because there would be no air resistance. Any colonist wishing to travel a few kilometres, would take a lift down into the 'ground', emerge, still inside the lift, through the wall of the space cylinder, travel out into empty space, and transfer via a pressurised air-lock to an air-tight vehicle. This would be a form of space-cab which travels along guidance rails on the outside surface of the cylinders. Each cab would be guided automatically by a computer guidance system, after the passenger has requested the desired destination by dialling a reference number into the computer. On arrival, the passenger would simply transfer to another lift to re-enter the cylinder. A different version of the space cab, which could carry passengers from one cylinder to the companion cylinder, could be released into free space and propelled by the rotational motion of the cylinder. This would eliminate the need for rocket engines or any other means of propulsion. The cab would reach the other cylinder at just the right time for it to be motionless relative to the moving surface of the second spinning cylinder. Naturally, there would need to be safeguards built into such a system to avoid the possibility of missing the target and flying on into space forever or colliding with the cylinder.

Not all cylinders would form complete human habitats. Some could be devoted exclusively to heavy industry, and others to business centres. Specialised cylinders could also be used as centres for learning and practising different trades and skills, and for education. Entire cylinders could even be used for agriculture. Food production cylinders would not necessarily maintain Earth gravity, neither would they need to observe the seasons. Climate, atmosphere, the length of the artificial day, soil quality and every other factor influencing agricultural production could be manipulated to give maximum farm yields. Some cylinders would be specialised for crop production, others for the rearing of animals, fish or poultry. The dream which present-day farmers may entertain in moments of fancy about controlling every factor influencing production on their farms could come true on the space colonies. Specialized colonies such as these could be highly profitable because they could cheaply export many commodities to Earth. To begin with, they could harness solar energy, convert it to electricity, and then divert it down to Earth on microwave beams. They could also be highly competitive in terms of industrial production. Specialised cylinders designed from the outset to have ideal conditions for particular manufacturing processes could ultimately produce goods more competitively than is possible on Earth. Food production cylinders could grow crops and animals free from diseases and pests and thus yield more than the future Earth could possibly produce. All of these extensions into the future give strength to the suggestion by Dr Gerard O'Neill and many other scientists that the space colonies would ultimately take over most of the work and everyday tasks from the mother planet, leaving Earth as a holiday resort, no more polluted or interfered with by industrial man than it has been already. Another great advantage is that future space colonists will not be displacing other life forms. Conservationists will, therefore, have no reason to complain about the new structes in Space. Furthermore, colonisation of Space would enable Earth to return to its more natural state: it would be feasible to ban the use of pesticides and other pollutants on Earth, and laws could decree that any new industrial processes be undertaken in Space. One footnote should be added, however. The space colonies would undoubtedly exploit the Moon, the Asteroids, and ultimately a great deal

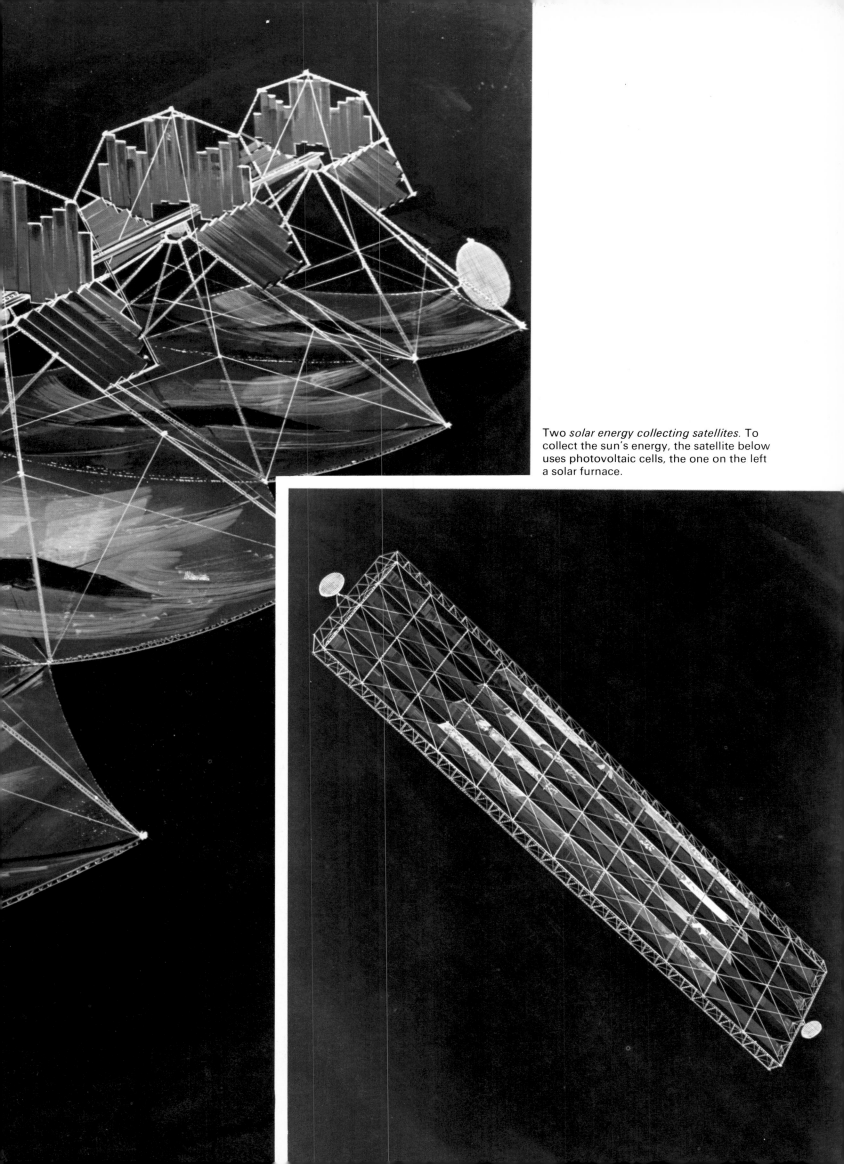

Two *solar energy collecting satellites*. To collect the sun's energy, the satellite below uses photovoltaic cells, the one on the left a solar furnace.

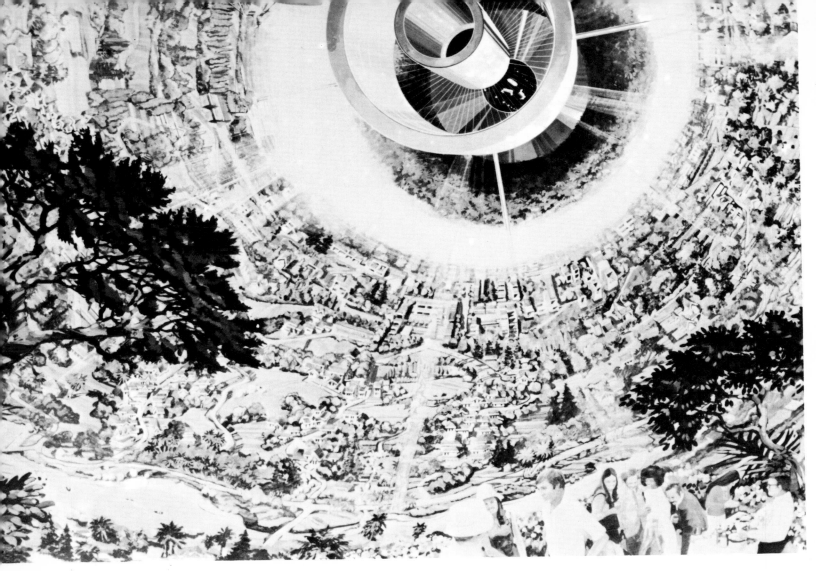

more of our solar system. Thus, the cause
of conserving these bodies may well be
denied for the sake of preserving human
life.

The question 'Will life on a space
colony be acceptable to the majority of
the human population?' is bound to be
asked. Space colonies have the potential
to fulfill many basic human needs.
Throughout history the world's population has been rising. This has been
interrupted from time to time by wars
and plagues, but the underlying trend
has been one of continually expanding
human population. Only now are we
faced with the need on Earth to halt this
growth. At the same time, advances in
nutrition and medicine have extended
the life expectancy of most people, so if
human life remains confined to this
planet, the proportion of old and middle
aged people will rise continually. This
could deny young people in the future
the challenges and opportunities which
have been freely open to their parents
and grandparents. There would simply
not be enough new opportunities to go
round. This would not mean that the
world would be any poorer, but young
people may eventually find life on Earth
unstimulating and boring. The space
colonies would provide a means of
avoiding this undesirable scenario, as
they could give scope once more for

unlimited challenges. The colonies could
also provide a great diversity of environ-
ments and lifestyles. Various political,
moral, religious and cultural differences
could exist from one autonomous colony
to another. There would be no need for
all to be ruled according to a uniform set
of values, provided they are willing to
cooperate in the vital areas of transport, communications, and the orderly
exploitation of resources. Colonists
would have greater freedom than most
citizens of the twentieth century, and the
potential diversity of lifestyles would
give scope for human ingenuity and
innovation on a grand scale. This experience may well give the human race the
start it needs in preparation for any
future expansion into our solar system
and ultimately, our Galaxy. However,
there are many problems which still have
to be resolved.

In space, even inside a cylinder,
humans would be subjected to larger
amounts of radiation. Earth's atmosphere
prevents many of the Sun's harmful rays
from reaching us and also gives us some
protection from high-energy cosmic rays
from deep in space. Special shields,
possibly incorporating magnetic or electric fields, may need to be constructed to
protect colonists, although experience
gained by astronauts so far shows no
deleterious effects from known space

Space offers a wealth of commercial possibilities both in terms of its raw materials and its natural properties. Once the difficulties of sustaining life in space for prolonged periods have been overcome the extraction of minerals from the moon or the asteroids, and the opportunities for the development and manufacture of new alloys using the natural vacuum, can be seriously considered.

Proposals for housing those engaged in such pursuits include this mile-long Bernal Sphere Colony. Surface gravity is provided by spinning the structure around its longitudainal axis, thereby creating suitable conditions for establishing a self-sufficient ecology with a high degree of environmental control.

Continuity of communication with such colonies could be ensured by siting them in areas known as Lagrangian Points, where the gravitational effects of Earth and the Moon combine to form stable positions.

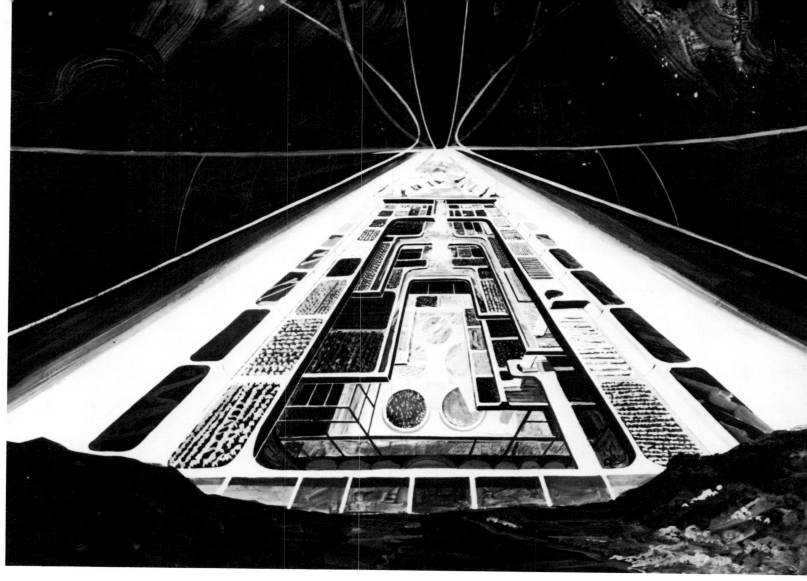

Above
Artist's impression of a Space Colony's *agricultural area* situated between two parks. Soya beans, wheat, sorghum, and other crops are grown on the top four levels of the farm. The bottom level is a drying facility. Water is supplied directly from the river and indirectly through the fish culture tanks that line the sides. Rabbits and cattle are also reared on the farm. Because moisture, sunlight, and heat conditions are controlled, the farm could yield far more than its equivalent on Earth, enabling the colony to produce enough food to be self sufficient.

Opposite
Cut-away of proposed *Bernal Sphere Space Colony* showing the park-like setting inside the sphere, and the non-rotating cosmic ray/solar flare shield on the outside.

radiation. Another problem may be caused by the rotation of the cylinders which provide artificial gravity by centrifugal force. It may turn out that such rotating systems will give the inhabitants of space colonies a form of permanent motion sickness. Hopefully, solutions to these problems will be resolved shortly.

Although the space colonies could provide ideal living conditions in many ways for most of the human race in the future, there would also be benefits from inhabiting the Moon and some of the planets and their moons. Dr Von Eshelman of Stanford University in California has calculated that both the Moon and Mars could be given artificial atmospheres which would make them suitable for human habitation without having to resort to the plastic or glass domes often described by science fiction writers. Although we are taught in school that the Moon doesn't have an atmosphere because its gravitational pull is too weak to retain any gases which may ever have existed, Dr Eshelman points out that any gases released on the Moon would nevertheless take a very long time to escape into space. The same is true of Mars, which already has a thin atmosphere. Since the Moon was formed, it has had more than 4,000 million years to allow any atmosphere to escape into

space. A man-made atmosphere on the Moon would take many thousands of years to escape – certainly long enough for the purposes of human colonisation. An atmosphere introduced onto Mars would last even longer. Dr Von Eshelman suggests that in many ways the planet Venus could prove to be ideal for human habitation. The temperature on the surface of Venus is hotter than an oven. In addition to this, the planet's atmosphere is a hundred times thicker than Earth's, and consists mostly of carbon dioxide. However, if the atmosphere could be reduced in mass and altered by introducing tiny, living organisms into the upper atmosphere which consume the carbon dioxide and produce oxygen (as suggested by the American astronomer, Carl Sagan), it may eventually become possible for humans to breathe on Venus. With an atmosphere no thicker than Earth's and having only traces of carbon dioxide, the surface temperature of Venus could be reduced to something approaching that of Earth. There may, of course, be a great many arguments, about whether man should take the liberty of interfering with nature to such an extent. Despite this, planetary engineering does seem possible, and the need to make use of other planets may seem of paramount importance to future human civilisation.

Food: The Quest for Abundance

Will Earth be able to feed her ever growing population in the future? At present, thousands of millions of people have to subsist on less than what many would regard as even a starvation diet. At first sight the outlook for the future seems bleak, but when examined in detail, the picture looks very different. More than enough food is being produced already to provide everybody on our planet with a good diet, and in the future, food production will more than be able to keep pace with population growth. Also, changing patterns of diet could extend still further the world's capacity to feed her millions.

World food production recently received a huge boost with the so-called Green Revolution of the 1950s and 1960s, when scientists selectively bred new varieties of such crops as wheat and rice which could yield twice as much food, or, in some instances, a great deal more, than older varieties. When grown with the help of fertilisers, a by-product of the oil industry, the new crops dramatically demonstrated that agricultural regions could produce far more food than had ever been thought possible in the past. On the evidence of present-day scientific work, a new Green Revolution is just around the corner, although it is not needed yet, the present-day problems of starvation and malnutrition in many countries are being caused by poverty and not by a shortage of food. Most of the world's starving millions live in cities where an abundance of foods can be bought, but a wide range of social and political problems prevent such people from obtaining money to buy food.

Paradoxically, the future growth of food production is expected to be made possible by a return in many places to old farming practices. The secret of future success lies in combining the best of traditional methods with newly-discovered scientific techniques. There are countless examples in present-day farming which illustrate what is to come.

One ancient farming technique poised to make a come-back is mixed cultivation. This is basically the practice which most good gardeners follow, growing a little of everything on quite a small area of land. Millions of small scale farmers, particularly in the less developed countries, still practise mixed cultivation. Meanwhile, in the developed countries, hundreds, or even thousands of hectares of land are often devoted exclusively to monocultures, the cultivation of single crops. But the trend has been resisted in many developing countries. In Jamaica, for example, crops of sugar cane and bananas have been grown in huge plantations, but hundreds of thousands of small farmers, owning only one hectare of land or even less, have grown these same crops mixed with twenty or more other staple foods. Now, despite a whole range of scientific measures aimed at boosting the production of plantation crops, the huge plantations of Jamaica have run into difficulties because of pests, poor yields, and a shortage of labour, but at the same time the small farms have flourished. The reason for the small farms' survival is basically simple: nature flourishes in diversity. Mixtures of plants and animals grow together in natural harmony and protect each other naturally from such catastrophes as pest infestation and drought. However, vast areas of farmland with single crops will undoubtedly continue to be important for future food supplies because not all regions are best suited to mixed cultivation. The wheatlands of America and the Soviet Union for example, will probably remain the principle 'breadbaskets' of the world for many years to come, but mixed cultivation on small farms may provide an ever increasing source of food, particularly in the developing countries where the food is most needed. In the past, such countries practising mixed cultivation have been denied the advantages of modern developments in farming, but in the future, it is likely that new crop varieties will be introduced specifically with the small farm in mind. These could be grown with the help of well-researched management and pest control techniques using fertilisers and vastly improved crop storage systems.

New methods of planting seeds will also become part of man's vast new armoury for increasing the world's

harvests. For example, the invention of the 'jelly drill', a system of planting seeds developed at the National Vegetable Research Station near Warwick in England, has given farmers much greater control over some crops. The method consists of germinating the seeds before they are planted, by soaking them in a nutrient jelly. Each seed develops a small root and shoot in the jelly, so that as soon as it reaches the soil it can begin growing. This means that the farmer can begin germinating his seeds before the weather is warm enough for planting, and then get them into the soil at the earliest possible time. This can save several weeks on traditional methods which, when dry seeds are planted, require several days during which moisture from the soil penetrates the seed and begins germination, and up to several weeks before the shoot and root emerge. Jelly drilling not only produces the germinating seed precisely when it is needed, but also makes it possible for farmers to harvest crops sooner and to grow some crops in places where they could not be grown previously. If the growing season is short, for example, jelly drilling enables farmers to take full advantage of whatever season there is. Thus, many parts of the world can grow crops which could not previously be grown. So far, this system has been used on only a small number of crops – asparagus, for example, thrives on it – and, hopefully, the jelly drill method will soon be in widespread use.

Plant breeding has already transformed agriculture in the twentieth century, and will almost certainly continue to be a source of major advances in food production. Crops suffer from many diseases, and in most cases they survive in spite of infection, but yields are seriously reduced. When strains of crops are successfully bred to resist the major diseases, increases in crop yields could be even more dramatic. The International Rice Research Centre in the Phillipines, where new varieties of high-yielding rice were developed, was a big contributor to the most recent Green Revolution. Present work, which includes the selective breeding of disease-free strains of rice, should help revive the Green Revolution once again. The International Centre for Cereals (CIMMYT) in Mexico also helped make the Green Revolution possible by developing high-yielding varieties of wheat and maize. But, as with rice, these miracle varieties have not fulfilled all of their early promise. In many instances, their enormously better yields could only be obtained with the use of fertilisers and unusually careful management techniques because the crops were often found to be more susceptible to disease, changes in the weather and other factors. Recently, however, CIMMYT has developed dwarf wheat and dwarf maize – crops which are already combining the high yields of Green Revolution varieties with superior

Above
With the development of *fluid drilling*, farmers have been able to germinate seeds before they are planted, enabling greater control over a large number of crops. The germinated seed can be produced precisely when it is needed.

Opposite top
After an earthquake, farmers in Nicaragua were encouraged to grow *high yielding varieties of maize* to combat increasing food shortages. This introduction brought both long and short term benefits to the farmers and economy of Nicaragua.

Opposite left
At the John Innes Institute in Norwich, England, a new variety of pea plant has been bred – without leaves. The *leafless pea* was developed after it was discovered that the pea has enough green parts (energy converting chlorophyl) in its pod to satisfy is growth potential.

This pea plant should enable farmers to produce high yields from a small area of land.

Opposite right
A *normal pea plant* with all of its leaves.

management characteristics such as easier harvesting and resistance to disease and to high winds (which could damage taller plants).

Another agricultural innovation is the pea plant without leaves which has been bred at the John Innes Institute near Norwich, England. The scientist responsible for this development, Professor John Davies, suggests that there are good reasons for exploiting such varieties in the future. All green plants grow by converting carbon dioxide from the air into carbon compounds. This is done by the process of photosynthesis under the action of sunlight in the green parts of the plant. The ordinary pea has quite enough green parts to provide all its growing capability without using leaves. So leafless peas are potentially more efficient at channelling the growth into producing peas rather than leafy structure. However, the completely leafless pea may not be ideally suited to farming needs, so the team at the John Innes Institute has conducted cross-breeding programmes with ordinary peas. The resulting product is a pea plant, with relatively few leaves, which retains most of the desirable characteristics, such as the flavour, of the best peas currently being grown commercially. The partially leafless pea plant has by no means taken over yet, but it is one of the candidates for future use which may help farmers squeeze the last fraction of productivity

Above
The need to greatly increase crop yields for future world food supplies has led to research into *plant regulators*, chemicals generally found naturally in plants. They control all phases of plant growth and development including seed germination, shoot and root growth, fruiting, and ripening. One chemical company, the Union Carbide Corp. is already marketing a plant regulator called ETHREL. This non-toxic chemical, when applied to plants, liberates ethylene, a hormone that is the plant's natural ripening agent. In the case of field-grown tomatoes, ETHREL accelerates early tomato ripening and promotes uniform colour development. The tomatoes of the picture on the right have been treated with ETHREL. Those on the left were untreated. The treated crop produced 95% red fruit. The untreated crop produced 60% red fruit.

Opposite
In *hydroponic farming*, plants are grown in a chemical fluid which contains all the nutrients needed to assist plant growth. This process, which will enable the farmer to control his crop and harvest precisely, may be a key factor in future world food supplies.

out of their land in the years ahead.

A key factor in increasing world food supplies in the future is the use of chemical growth regulators on crops. It has been discovered that, like animals, plants possess hormones, naturally occurring chemicals which circulate within the plants and control different aspects of growth. Some of the plant hormones promote growth, others inhibit it. In their natural state, plants need to control their growth to take maximum advantage of natural conditions. In periods of drought, for example, plants produce growth retardants which inhibit further growth until the drought is over. When conditions are good, with adequate sunlight and rainfall, the plants generate growth promoting hormones. By artificially using these substances, man can now exert greater control over crop growth than ever before.

One of the best-known plant hormones is ethylene. This is involved with the ripening process. The Union Carbide Company now markets a compound called Ethrel which is applied to crops by spraying and yields ethylene on contact with the plants. This gives farmers control over ripening, making it possible for them to choose precisely the date of harvest; to make sure that all the crops ripen at the same time, and, over a period of several years, to produce higher

yields. Scientists working on the whole range of plant hormones are developing synthetic compounds which can manipulate every stage of the plant growth, from root and shoot formation, through early growth of the plant, to flowering and fruiting. At the Plant Breeding Institute near Cambridge, England, scientists are using a growth regulator called Chlormequat to thicken the stems of dwarf wheats. The research which has produced dwarf cereals is thus being aided by the use of chemicals to perfect the crops. The dwarf varieties have already proven superior to the taller varieties in terms of yield and disease resistance. They are also better at resisting being flattened by high winds, but the growth regulators make the plants yet more sturdy and more capable of providing the future world with reliable food supplies.

In England and elsewhere, a revolution in fruit growing is also in progress. As with the wheat and maize in Mexico, there has been a trend all over the world towards cultivating varieties of apple trees which are as short as possible. One of the main reasons for this is to facilitate the use of mechanical harvesters. At the Long Ashton Research Centre near Bristol, England, the process has been taken to the extreme with what have often been called meadow apples. The new super-dwarf varieties of apple trees

One of the *Greensleeves dwarf apple trees*, a new variety developed by East Malling Research Station in Kent, England. The cultivation of such trees will facilitate mechanical harvesting and economise on growth space. The apples produced are the same size and in the same abundance as on a normal apple tree. The dwarfing of trees is achieved by grafting the bud of a desired apple variety onto the root of another variety. This is called a rootstock.

and the tree itself. The tree which produces the desired variety of apple is grafted onto a root system which has the best growing performance. The East Malling scientists have developed a rootstock called Malling 27 which produces dwarf trees, making very high-density orchards possible. Malling 27 is described in the trade as a 'precocious' variety of root. This means that it grows quickly and soon reaches maturity. The East Malling scientists have also developed a precocious variety of apple which they call Greensleeves which, when grafted onto the dwarf rootstock Malling 27, produces an ideal combination for orchards of dwarf trees that come to maturity and yield large harvests of fruit within two years. This development is still only at the research stage at present, but during the coming decades it seems likely that many of the world's orchards will start growing these dwarf trees. Similar techniques, it is hoped, can ultimately be applied to other fruits. The main advantage is that the trees can make better use of the available sunlight for growing and so yield much greater quantities of fruit on any area of ground.

The other modern tool which is combined with breeding programmes is the production of plants by laboratory culture techniques without the use of seeds. At the East Malling Research Station and at many other research centres concerned with fruit growing, certain laboratory tissue culture techniques have become a routine means of growing large numbers of a new variety of tree. Tiny segments of the tree being reproduced are placed in laboratory cultures of nutritive fluids, each one producing a whole plant. Over 100,000 apple rootstocks can now be produced from a single shoot tip within a year. The fact that it is no longer necessary to wait until a tree produces seeds before large numbers can be reproduced, means that in the future, farmers will be able to rapidly increase fruit tree production when necessary. At East Malling, scientists are also aiming to reproduce, by means of these laboratory tissue culture techniques, coconut trees without the use of seed. So far, the efforts have not met with success, but if the technique is perfected, it could be a boon to countries which have been ravaged by such devastating coconut diseases as lethal yellowing which can completely destroy a generation of trees. Such techniques could drastically reduce the impact of such disasters.

being produced there are planted closely together in fields – almost like a crop of potatoes. Whereas the apple 'trees' are kept very small by the use of chemicals which retard their growth, the fruit is nevertheless the same as it would be when produced on a large tree. However, the plants reach maturity and produce fruit in less than two years, and harvesting can be done by cutting down the whole tree, which may be less than a metre high.

Another glimpse into the future of fruit growing can be seen at the East Malling Research Station in Kent, England, where apple trees are grown in orchards with only half a metre between each of the dwarf trees. The trees themselves stand only chest high and produce fruit within two years of planting. This has all been made possible by the combination of a number of different laboratory techniques. It is not often realised that the modern fruit tree is a combination of two parts: the root-stock

As crop production throughout the world rises, the pressure to use lands which have not previously been considered suitable for agricultural production becomes even greater. In many coastal areas, where the climates are ideal for growing crops, the soils suffer from high concentrations of salt which make it impossible to grow ordinary varieties of many crops. Also, arid regions which have been extensively irrigated in the past suffer from a gradual build-up of salt in the ground. To get over this problem, salt tolerant crops are being bred. At the University of California's Davis campus, Jack Norlyn and Don Fredrickson have bred varieties of barley and tomatoes which can tolerate very salty water. They can grow even in water more salty than sea water. The varieties produced so far still need to be used in further cross-breeding programmes before ideal crops for farming are produced, but the remarkable success of the early research holds out the hope that in the future many salty lands will be opened up for crop production.

Another example of how previously useless land can be used for intensive crop production can be seen on the tiny island of Sadiyat in the Arabian Gulf, where an enormous variety of vegetables are being grown inside huge plastic greenhouses, using a number of techniques planned by scientists from the University of Arizona. Electrical fans and air conditioning units keep the temperature right, and fresh water is supplied from the sea by means of diesel generators which provide electrically-produced heat to evaporate the sea water and hence remove the salt. This valuable salt-free water is not lost to the atmosphere because it stays trapped within the greenhouses, and every drop is used. Even carbon dioxide from the diesel exhaust fumes is put to good use. It is separated from the exhaust pollutants and fed into the greenhouses to enrich the atmosphere and promote better plant growth. Fertilisers are also used extensively to make up for the lack of nutrients in the desert sands. This is not the cheapest way to produce vegetables, but in places where they could otherwise be obtained only by air transport from distant countries, the economics of such a system are excellent. As the world's need for food increases in the coming years desert greenhouses may become one of the many ways of getting the most benefit from land which is available.

Even without improving plant growth and crop yields, there is another important means by which world food supplies can be vastly increased in the future. At present, a large proportion of the world's harvest is destroyed by pests. Estimates vary, many experts putting the figure at about half of the world's production, but even this proportion is an improvement on past records. Chemical pesticides such as DDT have reduced pest infestations greatly during the last few decades, but it

is feared that the present levels of such chemicals in the environment may be too high. DDT and other so-called organochlorine pesticides can sometimes be concentrated by natural processes. Insects, birds, and animals can absorb the pesticides and accumulate them. When such pesticides accumulate inside farm animals, the health of the humans who eat them is also threatened. Thus, scientists around the world are looking towards new methods of pest control which do not involve the increasing use of chemical pesticides.

Much hope for this project lies with the technique called biological pest control, in which natural enemies of pests are introduced in order to eliminate them. A dramatic, if horrific, example of biological pest control at its most effective took place in Britain and Australia during the 1950s when both countries had been plagued by very large numbers of rabbits which were destroying vast quantities of valuable crops. The highly

A European rabbit with *myxomatosis*, a highly infectious virus which was artificially introduced into the wild rabbit population of Britain and Australia in the 1950's. In this test of biological pest control, the hordes of rabbits, which were ruining quantities of valuable crops, were practically annihilated. The survivors have never since exceeded a pest control limit, but some have developed a resistance to the disease.

In the search for increasing future food supplies, much land is being reclaimed from the sea. However, the reclaimed land has a high salt content and must be irrigated with a great deal of fresh water before plants can be grown successfully. To combat this problem, scientists have been breeding *salt tolerant crops*. They have been very successful with the tomato plant, so much so that new strains have been grown in water more salinated than the sea.

In the picture, tomatoes are being grown in a reclaimed swamp in the Everglades, Florida (the polythene is to keep the moisture in).

Research by the Weir Group in Glasgow, Scotland into new methods of water desalination led to the development of a process called *flash distillation* which is based on the fact that water can be made to boil just as effectively by reducing pressure as by raising its temperature. In fact, if water and steam are together in a closed vessel their temperature and pressure are so inter-related that any reduction in pressure will cause instantaneous boiling of some of the water, with the characteristic 'flashing' effect:

Heating steam (1) (usually from a power station) heats the sea-water in the heat input section (2) and is then discharged (3). The hot sea-water is passed through a series of 'flash chambers', each at a lower pressure and temperature than the last, in the heat recovery section (4). In each chamber (there may be from 16 to 40), some of the water 'flashes' into vapour, rises through demisters which remove any droplets of salt water, condenses on condenser tubes and is collected as fresh water (7). In the last few stages, during the heat rejection process (5), cold, raw sea-water is pumped (8) through the condenser tubes to lower the temperature enough for condensation to take place and to extract an amount of heat equal to that added in the heat input section. Thus, a continuous cycle of operation takes place. Non-condensible gases are extracted from the flash chambers by a vacuum pump or steam jet air ejector (6). Some of the raw sea-water is discharged to waste(9) and some is used to replace evaporation losses in the main system (1) after being treated with chemical additives(11) to control scale formation. After leaving the last flash chamber (5), part of the sea-water is recirculated (12) through the condenser tubes in the heat recovery section (4) and part is discharged to waste (13).

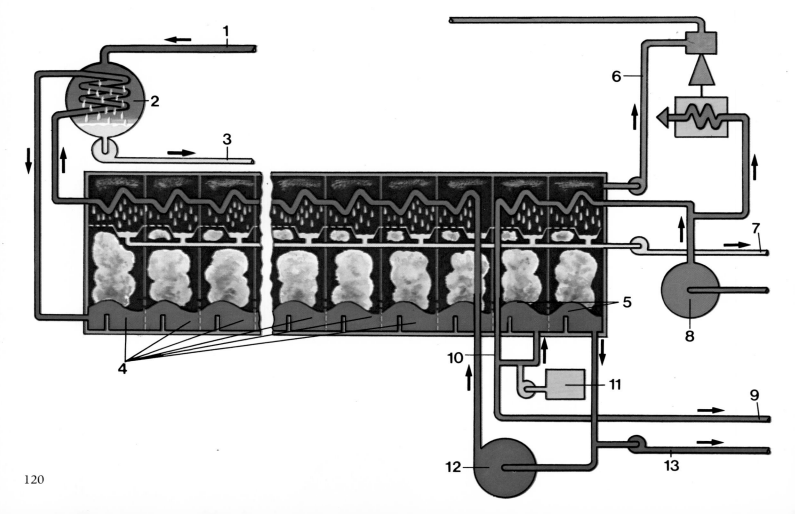

Above
An artist's impression of a colony of *floating greenhouses* which could be moored off the coasts of arid countries for the production of fruit and vegetable crops at a fraction of the cost of present imports. The greenhouses might contain devices such as: wind turbines and solar panels to produce and store electricity; computer-controlled shades to regulate sunlight; and reverse-osmosis desalination units to provide fresh water.

Right
The *cultivation of arid land*, such as the deserts in Arizona, U.S.A., will play a major part in the search for increased food production.

Above
The *biological control* of a major coconut pest, in this case weeds, was achieved by sowing leguminous plants between rows of replanted coconut trees. Both the legume and the coconut are harvested, enhancing the food productivity of the land.

Right
Leaf cutting ants feeding on citrus leaves show how seriously ants can damage valuable crops.

infectious virus disease myxomatosis was then introduced into wild rabbit populations. At the height of the artificially introduced epidemic, which led to the almost total annihilation of the rabbit, corpses were littered across the countryside. However, the animal survived, and populations have remained below pest proportions ever since.

When pests become a problem, it is often as a result of the farming methods being used. All pests have natural enemies, and if farmers cultivate regions in such a way that conditions for the pest are ideal whereas conditions for the pest's natural enemies are adverse, the result is that pest populations will rise. Biological control is a means by which nature's balance can be restored, and for complete success it often needs to be accompanied by changes in farming methods. Crop rotation is a practice which is now regaining popularity among farmers, not only because of the beneficial effects on soil fertility, but also because of the help it gives in reducing pests. Wherever a larger variety of crops is grown, the infestations from any one pest species are smaller. Crop rotation and the move back to small-scale farming are accordingly being recommended by modern agricultural scientists. The pest control problem is yet another reason why the best of traditional farming practices may in the future be combined with modern developments in agricultural science.

As well as myxomatosis, biological pest control has many other recent successes. In 1971, a new coconut pest, a beetle known as Promecotheca, was accidentally introduced into Sri Lanka. Scientists did not take long to find reports that a similar beetle had been controlled in Fiji by the introduction of two parasites of the Promecotheca. At very little cost, the parasites were introduced to Sri Lanka with the result that within a very short period of time the island was saved from huge coconut losses. However, because of their vast territorial expanses, mainland countries may not be able to eliminate pests so easily. In the near future, international bodies such as the United Nations may well be as much concerned with the world war against pests as they are about conflicts between member nations. International pest control efforts could eventually protect against situations in which neighbouring countries, with different patterns of agricultural development, may be hindering each other's pest problems. World control of pests, and world planning of the pattern of farming, could go a long way in the future towards guaranteeing better harvests for all countries.

Recently, computers for planning biological control have joined in the battle against pests. At York University in England, biologists have been using computers to simulate the conflict between insect pests and organisms called parasitoids, creatures that lay their eggs in the eggs or larvae of the pest insects. The growing parasitoid eats its host's eggs and thus reduces the pest populations. Parasitoids have been found to be among the most effective biological control agents. The aim of the York scientists was to find the best way of using them by simulating countless battles within the computer between pest and parasitoid. By careful comparison with results obtained from real life introductions of parasitoids in different parts of the world, the scientists have been able to programme their computer to give specific recommendations of how to introduce such agents and which type of parasitoid will be most effective. One factor found to be important is that the parasitoid should not be too efficient at killing off its host. Otherwise, it will be left after a short period of time with no food to eat. Both pest and parasitoid then die out in the short term, leaving no protection in the long term should the

Maize smut, a killer fungus, shown here on its host, is a good candidate for future developments in pest control. The grey/white bulbous protruberances are the fungii.

Although space offers a host of exciting opportunities, the oceans of Earth still represent a vast and underexploited resource. Its potential as a largescale source of food has only been partially developed and the world's soaring population levels could lead to a fresh examination of our use of the sea.

Intensive and largescale undersea farming could replace traditional fishing techniques which rely heavily on the natural provision of adequate supplies. Apart from ensuring that existing species of fish are maintained in sufficient quantities, new varieties and breeds could be developed to supplement the foods provided by intensive cultivation of the land.

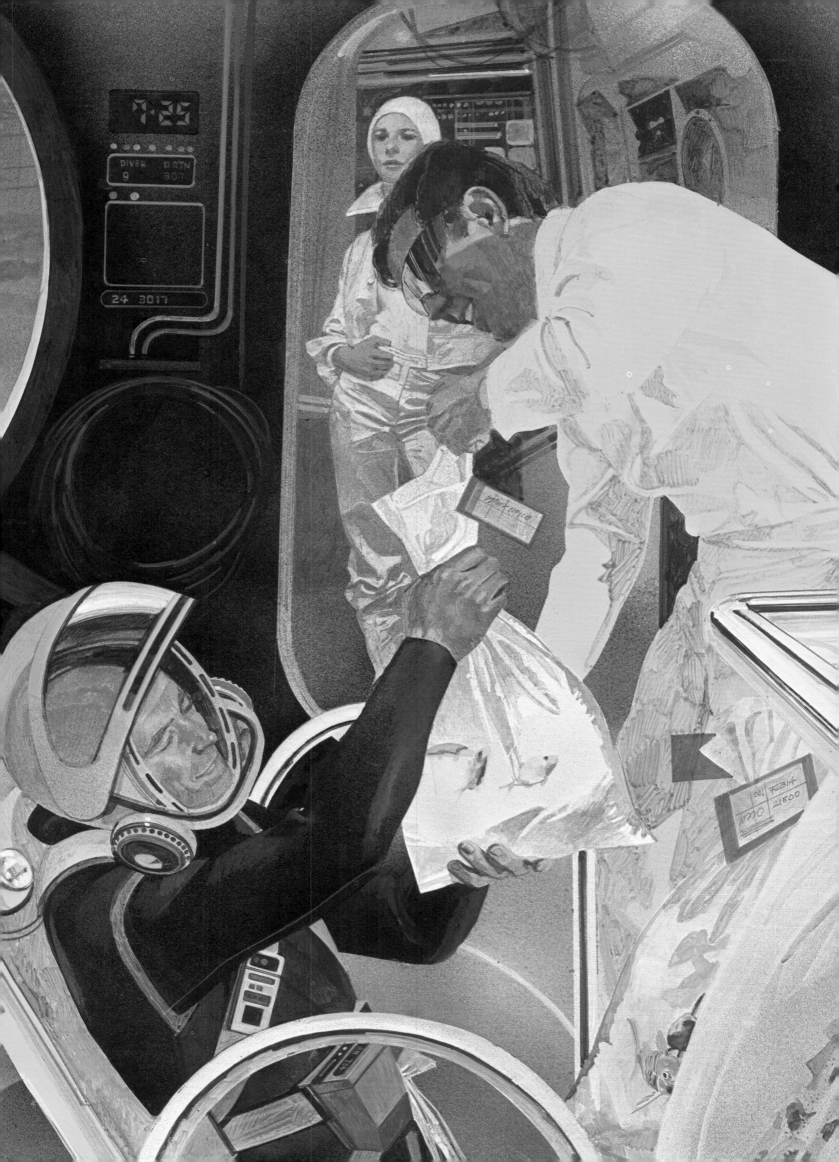

High quality sheep raised at a government research station in Argentina are the result of *cross-breeding* between indigenous and imported New Zealand sheep. They are raised for meat and wool, both of which are better in quality and quantity.

pest ever be accidentally introduced again. The most effective natural enemies of pests are those which remain in the pest populations at a sub-lethal level, keeping populations down, and remaining ready to multiply if ever the pest should get out of hand again.

A simple example is that of the tick bird of Africa. For countless centuries, this bird has been helping wild animals by sitting on their backs and eating the ticks which make their homes in the animals' skins. When cattle were introduced to many African countries, ticks became an enormous problem: they caused retarded growth, and transmitted debilitating diseases between animals. Twentieth century scientific techniques solved this problem by treating the animals with chemical pesticides to kill the ticks. Unfortunately, however, the tick birds not only lost their source of food but were also poisoned by the chemicals and died out in their thousands. The tick's natural enemy had been lost, and cattle ticks soon multiplied out of all proportion, requiring ever larger doses of chemical pesticides to control them. The situation has now turned full circle with the realisation that tick bird populations must be boosted once again to provide a reliable and inexpensive method of tick control. Chemical pesticides are still being used, but compounds not poisonous to tick birds have been substituted for earlier chemicals which helped kill off a great number of the birds. Also, farmers take care to keep enough ticks alive to provide an adequate diet for the birds. By manipulating natural enemies in this way, farmers of

the future may be able to create a world of very high plant and animal food production that is not heavily contaminated by pesticides.

Animals require more land to produce a given amount of food than do crop harvests, and because of this, in the future, crops which humans can eat are likely to become relatively more important than the production of animal crops and animals. Wherever animals are fed crops grown on land which could be used for the higher-yield production of human food, there will always be the possibility that in the future animals will gradually be removed as a source of food. Nevertheless, because many agricultural regions are well suited to the growing of fodder crops and could not easily be converted to growing food crops for humans, it seems likely that it will never be necessary for the human race to adopt a totally vegetarian diet. Furthermore, animal production is likely to become increasingly efficient. Intensive production of poultry is already well advanced, and thanks to the introduction of 'broiler-house' techniques for rearing the birds, chicken meat has become a cheap commodity.

In the future, many other animals are likely to be intensively reared in disease-free buildings with automated feeding and cleaning arrangements, air conditioning, and computerised monitoring of every aspect of the animals' feeding, health, and growth. Already, great steps forward in animal rearing have been made possible by the use of artificial insemination which helps guarantee the quality of the animals. In the case of cattle, for example, high quality bulls, having the best available genetic characteristics, can be mated with large numbers of cows to allow the rapid production of calves which possess the superior qualities of both parents.

Manipulation of desirable genetic characteristics could become even more efficient in the future, with the aid of laboratory techniques such as those currently being developed at the Institute of Animal Physiology in Cambridge, England, where Dr Bob Moore and colleagues have perfected a technique for removing live eggs from recently slaughtered sheep. The eggs are treated with hormones and nutrients in the test tube to make them mature — ready for fertilisation — as they would do in the live animal. They are then transferred to live sheep which have just been mated and thus have live sperm within them capable of fertilising the eggs from the dead sheep. The technique makes it possible to produce a much greater proportion of twins with the result that meat production can be increased. The same methods are also being tested on cattle and could result in an even greater economic return than that produced by the sheep experiments. One great advantage of the already proven sheep method is that eggs can be obtained in the slaughterhouse from sheep having superior genetic characteristics but being too old to bear lambs themselves. When the eggs are fertilised with sperm from the best rams, the resultant lambs are of even better quality than those produced by artificial insemination. There is also the possibility that eggs removed in the slaughterhouse could be frozen until needed, guaranteeing the production of high quality animals at any time in the future.

The method may even be used for cloning, the reproduction of identical animals from the living cells of selected parents. The nucleus of an egg could be removed and replaced with genetic material from an animal from which a 'carbon copy' is required. This would mean that any animal found to have the ideal characteristics required by the farmer could be reproduced indefinitely to make thousands, or hundreds of thousands of 'copies'. This method would ultimately take all of the chance element out of the process of animal breeding and guarantee farmers perfect animals every time.

Another recent development is likely to bring forward the day when farm animals can be mass-produced to order. Dr David Whittingham of the Medical Research Council's Mammalian Development Unit in London, working in co-operation with colleagues in the United States, has developed techniques for storing living animal embryos. They are deep-frozen for several years at the temperature of liquid nitrogen, – 196 °C, and subsequently raised as normal young after being transplanted into foster mothers. This has proved highly successful in mice, and the same technique promises to be applicable to other mammals including farm animals. This means that living embryos of superior animals, needed for meat production, could in the future be stored in large numbers as part of an overall programme aimed at producing reliable supplies of farm animals.

As with human food crops, there is good reason to believe that in the next century we shall produce and eat a great deal more fish than at present. Whatever improvements are made in animal production, meat will remain a luxury item for most of the world's population. Fish, on the other hand, could emerge as one of our main sources of protein since, for a variety of reasons, they produce protein from their food more efficiently than animals. They are cold blooded, so they don't need to waste energy keeping themselves warm. Their weight is supported by the water, so they don't use up energy moving about to the extent which land animals do. If the comparison is drawn between fishing and the ancient practice of hunting animals for meat which gave way to farming animals, it seems obvious that fish farms could

Above

The common Asian practice of combining *sewage treatment with fish culture* could provide many tropical countries, where this method is most efficient, with an improved diet and healthier conditions. The I.R.D.C. (International Rice Development Council) has been investigating the capabilities of the system in countries such as Israel, Peru and India. As well as allowing reclamation and re-use of water and an expanded production capacity, the scheme offers revenue opportunities to offset waste treatment costs.

Left

The Water Hyacinth has for many years been thought of only as a problem weed because of its prodigious growth rate. On the lower reaches of the River Nile in Egypt, special precautions have to be taken to ensure that the plant does not block navigation. However, it is exactly this property that makes it an ideal candidate for exploitation. The Chinese are growing it in great quantities in ditches and swamps for use as an animal feed or, when fermented, as a fertilizer. In the Everglades in Florida, U.S.A., large areas of swamp have been fenced off for the cultivation of the Water Hyacinth as a food for the manatee or dugong — sea cows — which can be caught as food for humans. NASA has also conducted experiments with the Water Hyacinth in which they have demonstrated the plant's capacity to purify water and its potential as a source of fuel.

ultimately yield far greater harvests than fish 'hunting'. At present, more than 90% of the world's fish comes from fish hunting, and there are already fears that the world's oceans are being over-fished. This may mean that the only method of increasing the world availability of fish will be large-scale development of fish farms all over the world.

The masters of fish farming are the Chinese who have been producing plant-eating fish for thousands of years. The Chinese have not adopted highly intensive systems, but simply release fish in flooded rice paddies, ponds, and ditches all over the country to take advantage of whatever food is available. In this way, large quantities of fish are produced at very low cost. Countries without such ideal conditions created by the cultivation of rice crops, could benefit greatly by projects such as the intensive farm for rainbow trout called Project Sheerwater, which has been set up by The British Oxygen Company in the north of England. This project's aim is to bring intensive fish rearing to the level of efficiency which has been achieved with poultry. The fish are fed on concentrated food pellets and every stage of their growth is carefully monitored. Since the fish tanks contain the same weight of living fish as they do water, systems like this are more competitively productive than fish hunting.

Perhaps the greatest potential lies in the farming of marine fish. Huge areas of sea could be enclosed for the purpose of fish culture, and this development could be facilitated if wave-energy devices become commonly used. Before this, however, bays and estuaries are likely to be ideal locations for fish farming.

The incentives for producing quite novel forms of food are also likely to be stronger in the future, and expansion of the range of meat substitutes which have already found their way into sausages, pies, and other convenience foods (with very few people realising it) will certainly take place. The soya bean is undoubtedly the most popular source of substitute meat protein at present, but in the future a great many more unusual proteins will compete for places on our dinner tables.

The British Petroleum Company has been manufacturing a yeast protein called Toprina, which is grown on oil, for several years. This substance is fed to chickens and pigs as a high-protein

Protein malnutrition, one of the Third World's main enemies, could be countered by the introduction and development of inexpensive *high protein food supplements*. In some of Thailand's child care centres, researchers have set up pilot schemes to examine the effect on health of textured mung protein (containing 60% protein) in the children's diet.

supplement to their normal diets, and there is no reason why humans should not also eat Toprina or yeast proteins like it. The British Petroleum product is made in the form of a dry powder, not a very appetising prospect for humans, but the task of converting this into a simulated steak is likely to be quite simple for tomorrow's chemical engineers. Already, the plastics industry has developed methods of converting plastics into materials having a wide range of physical and mechanical properties. Extrusion and weaving processes, following chemical methods of linking cells of yeast together to form strands of protein, could soon produce foods which would appeal to most people. Of course, the availability of such proteins would depend on the production of oil throughout the world, but carefully selected grains of yeast could be grown on large quantities of low grade oil which are not easily suitable for use as fuels or chemical feedstocks. The world's oil residues could thus form the basis of industrial protein production for

perhaps hundreds of years into the future, long after oil has ceased to be a cheap, convenient source of energy and chemicals.

The problem of supplying the world with protein starts with the process of extracting nitrogen from the air. Nitrogen is essential to the structure of protein. It is also present in fertilisers. Plants absorb nitrogen from fertilisers, manure, and from the air to make nitrogen compounds and plant proteins. Animals and other organisms such as the yeasts and microfungi turn these compounds into edible proteins. Animals which eat carbohydrate fodder crops convert them into meat protein, but the conversion is slow and inefficient. However, many bacteria, yeasts, and other fungi can convert carbohydrates, of which there is an abundant supply, into proteins quickly and efficiently.

The Rank Hovis McDougall Company in Britain has developed a fermentation process that turns waste carbohydrate foods into edible protein. They use

organisms called microfungi, which grow on carbohydrate nutrients in special tanks kept at the right temperature, and control other conditions to speed the fermentation process. The microfungi have the advantage over yeasts and bacteria of producing filaments of protein which can more easily be structured to give textures similar to meat, fish, and other more conventional foods. Almost any carbohydrate food can be used for growing the microfungi: potatoes, sugar, casava, or any crop easily grown where the protein is needed. The cost of producing such protein is about one-tenth the cost of meat. Nutritionists don't agree yet about whether such novel proteins are an adequate substitute for meat, but in places where meat is almost impossible for most people to obtain, microfungi-based foods may fill an important need in the future.

Another method of recycling food resources is to take advantage of the fact that human and animal excrement contains very high concentrations of nitrogen compounds. One method of regenerating edible proteins is to grow organisms called algae on sewage wastes. It may be difficult to make such products acceptable to humans, but as a form of animal food they could be excellent. At the University of California's Berkeley campus, Professor William Oswald, who has been working on the production of algae from chicken effluent, has found that the resulting protein can be used as a supplement to pig feeds. In several places around the world, another system is being tried in which droppings from water birds such as ducks feed shell-fish which live on the pond bottoms. These droppings also have nutrients that help weeds, which herbiverous fish such as carp eat, grow on the pond surface. In this way, fish and poultry proteins can be obtained very efficiently with relatively little capital outlay.

The quest to extract more nitrogen from the air, and hence produce more protein, is being assisted by research aimed at increasing the efficiency with which plants absorb, or 'fix', atmospheric nitrogen. Plants such as legumes do this quite naturally with the help of bacteria which live within their roots. A mutually beneficial relationship exists between the bacteria and the plants: the bacteria help absorb atmospheric nitrogen and convert it into nitrogen compounds, while the plants create the ideal environment in which the bacteria can flourish. But many of the world's crops, such as the cereals, don't fix nitrogen naturally in this way. Accordingly, they need to be grown in fertiliser or manure in order to produce adequate growth and

Above

Nitrogen fixation

The presence of protein in plants is brought about through the action of symbiotic bacteria fixing nitrogen from the air. The process is quite normal and occurs naturally in leguminous crops. However, research is being carried out to effect this process in crops, such as cereals, which do not fix nitrogen naturally. The National Vegetable Research Station in Warwick, England, is using the fluid drilling proess to fix nitrogen in bean plants pictured here. The fluid carrier is innoculated with a desirable strain of bacteria which in turn invades the roots of the pre-germinated beans. Following invasion, the roots form nodules in which the bacteria is confined, and where nitrogen

fixation takes place. This process obviates the need for expensive, oil-based nitrogen fertilizers which could prevent world starvation when the oil runs out.

protein content. Professor John Postgate at Sussex University in England is director of the Unit of Nitrogen Fixation which is conducting research aimed at increasing the ability of plants to fix atmospheric nitrogen. There is hope that one day many of the crops which currently have to be treated with large quantities of fertilisers will be altered genetically to enable them to fix their own nitrogen directly from the air in the same way that legumes do. As fertilisers are currently obtained from such raw materials as oil, which may in the future be in short supply, this research could save the world from starvation when the oil runs out.

Much of the hope for manipulating the characteristics of future crops lies in the laboratory techniques of so-called genetic engineering. All living cells contain the genetic material called DNA which contains the blueprint for an organism's characteristics. Since the structure of some types of DNA was first analysed at the Molecular Biology Laboratory in Cambridge, England in the 1950s, a huge world effort aimed at understanding every aspect of the genetic characteristics of living organisms has been in progress. Genetic engineering is the artificial altering of the genetic material, the DNA, of a living cell, and thus the altering of the organisms that are built up from the cells. Much initial work has been done on bacteria, and recently, work at the Plant Breeding Institute in Cambridge, England, has been conducted on yeasts. These could be engineered to obtain better yeast proteins, or yeasts more suitable for fermentation. In the future, genetic engineering on plants themselves could eventually yield varieties which could fix atmospheric nitrogen, and have growing characteristics superior to naturally available varieties. This would be a departure from traditional plant breeding techniques in which nature's enormous variety of plant types are exploited for the purposes of selective cross-breeding. By performing genetic engineering, scientists could artificially manufacture the crop varieties they need without having to hunt for plants with the specific characteristics necessary for cross-breeding. However, all of this work must be done with considerable caution, for it is possible that dangerous bacteria, yeasts, and plants could be developed accidentally and pose a threat to the world. But the potential of the technique is clear: as scientists gradually accumulate knowledge about the genetics of plants, animals, and other organisms, they should eventually be able to help farmers guarantee world food supplies for many centuries to come.

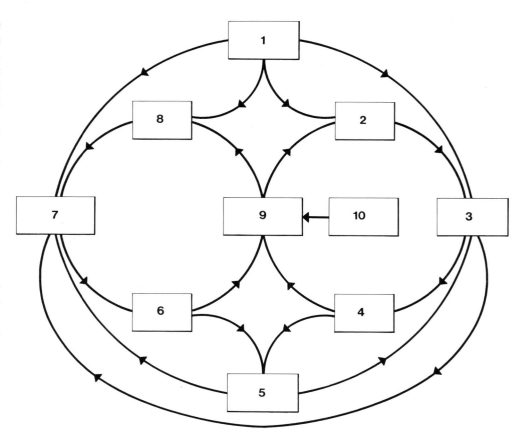

Top
Diagram of a food cycle: (1) crop production, (2) animal feed, (3) animal production, (4) farm effluent, (5) fresh water, (6) urban sewage, (7) human consumption, (8) food factory, (9) single-celled protein, (10) petroleum by-products.

Above
New forms of protein are easily converted into familiar looking convenience foods. This deep-fried breaded 'chicken' is in fact made from *mycoprotein*, a fibrous substance produced from mycrofungi, organisms that feed on carbohydrates.

The Medical Revolution

The human body represents one of the last frontiers for modern science. It is so complex that basic chemical and physical processes going on within the body are only just beginning to be understood by scientists and doctors. A huge variety of illnesses cannot be cured or treated effectively, and many diseases are on the increase, with doctors powerless to intervene. Perhaps more than any other branch of science or technology, medicine offers the greatest scope for improvement in the future world.

Fortunately, there are grounds for optimism about the future of medicine. To begin with, diagnosis seems poised to reach near-perfection during the coming decades. Doctors already possess a vast armoury of diagnostic equipment and laboratory tests which were only fantastic concepts even twenty years ago, and such technology is still developing rapidly. The area which looks the most promising at present is in so-called non-invasive methods of diagnosis, techniques in which bodily malfunctions and illnesses can be accurately diagnosed without surgical investigation.

One of the biggest diagnostic aids for future doctors could be the computer. Whereas all doctors inevitably have areas of strength and weakness when it comes to diagnosis, being familiar with some illnesses more than others, computers can be programmed to be comprehensive and unbiased in their approach to a patient. The future doctor's surgery may eventually look more like the cockpit of a space craft than the familiar room of today. At the touch of a button, doctors may be able to view notes, analyses, and calculations on a television-type display screen which will ensure that their judgement is backed up by detailed fact, and also perform many tests which today are normally done only in hospitals. Additionally medications could be prescribed with the help of a comprehensive check-list of all possible treatments, judged in the light of their known effects and side effects, and taking full consideration of the individual patient's condition and medical history. In many situations, however, the doctor of the future may hand over work

entirely to the computer. Patients could communicate directly with computers, and current evidence shows, surprisingly, that many patients are very happy to be interviewed initially by a 'computer doctor'. Computer doctors have been possible for a long time, but only since the development of the silicon chip, have they become potentially less costly than their human counterparts.

In Britain, a computer doctor named Mickie has already been introduced with remarkable success. It was developed by a group of scientists led by Dr Chris Evans of the National Physical Laboratory, near London. They set up a department called the Man Computer Interaction Group in 1968, and since then have been researching a variety of means by which humans can benefit from communicating directly with computers. In the case of Mickie, patients sit in front of the device and answer questions which are displayed on a teleprinter by the computer. The patient merely replies: 'Yes', 'No', or 'Don't know', in reply to each question by pressing the appropriate button on the computer. Mickie takes note of all the responses and delivers a printed sheet of information to the doctor who will eventually interview the patient again. At the Southern General Hospital in Glasgow, where Professor Wilfred Card tried interviewing patients by computer in 1969, most patients liked being questioned by the computer as much as or even more than by a human doctor. In its present form, Mickie is merely an aid to conventional medical interviewing, but Dr Evans believes there would be no difficulty in increasing the computer's ability to one of diagnosis. A few extra silicon chips wired into Mickie's circuitry could enable it to process the patients' replies and come up with diagnoses and recommended treatments. Chris Evans' group is also hoping to produce a miniature Mickie which could be fully portable and carried around like a pocket calculator. They have already produced a portable non-medical computer which could be mass-produced at a cost of a few dollars per unit. The future doctor could carry a miniature Mickie with him on house calls

Opposite top
In the *futuristic offices of London dentist* Peter Hunter, patients are treated while lying on a water bed heated to body temperature. The dentist, who works sitting down, uses ultrasonically cleaned instruments which are piped to the treatment room through a compressed air despatch system.

Opposite bottom
A new concept in dentistry, anticipative of future trends, has been implemented at several London clinics. These *high-technology surgeries* combine patient comfort with computer-controlled efficiency. The offices, which are constructed from fibreglass modular units, and monitored by a closed-circuit TV-system, contain a visual display readout screen in every room, providing instant access to patients' records and appointment schedules stored in the computer. All of the clinic's medical supplies are stored in a large, electrically controlled filing cabinet with rotating shelves. Whenever an item is removed, the computer notes its description, and when supplies run low, orders refills by printing out a letter addressed to the manufacturer, and then passing it to a folding and envelope-inserting machine. Appointments, monthly check-up reminders, and payroll are handled in the same way.

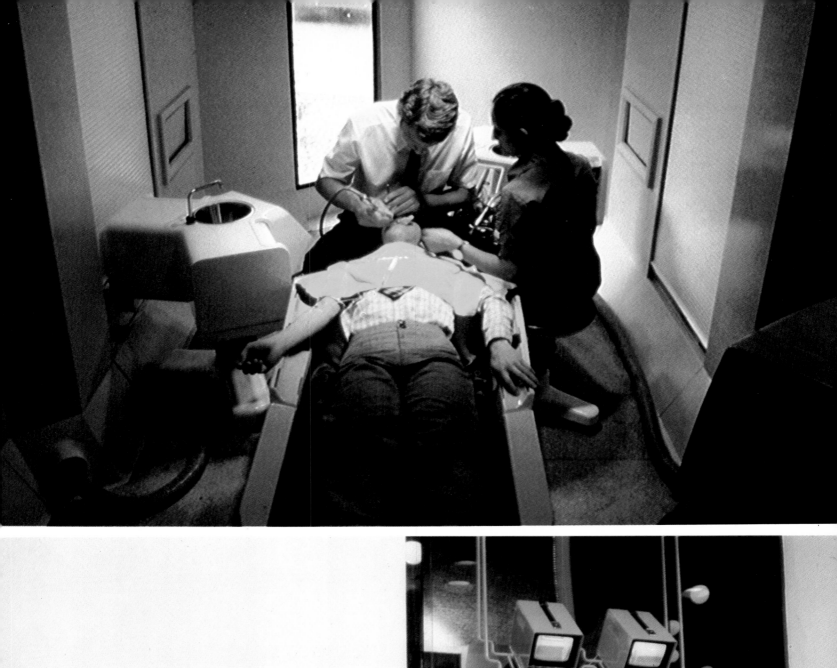

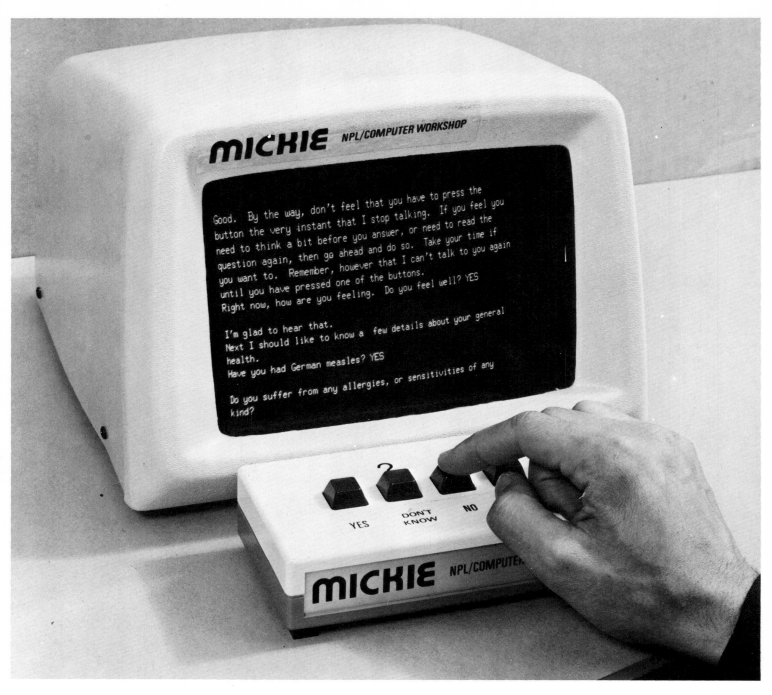

On the screen:

Good. By the way, don't feel that you have to press the button the very instant that I stop talking. If you feel you need to think a bit before you answer, or need to read the question again, then go ahead and do so. Take your time if you want to. Remember, however that I can't talk to you again until you have pressed one of the buttons.
Right now, how are you feeling. Do you feel well? YES

I'm glad to hear that.
Next I should like to know a few details about your general health.
Have you had German measles? YES

Do you suffer from any allergies, or sensitivities of any kind?

and so retain computer facilities even when away from the surgery. To give such portable devices full access to medical records and additional computing facilities, the visiting doctor could link it up to the computer via the patient's telephone. In this way, there would be practically no limit to the amount of computer power he would be able to use for diagnosing and recommending treatment.

The National Physical Laboratory team is also developing a voice recognition computer which could be programmed to recognise key words spoken by the doctor which could then be used as basic data for diagnosis, note taking, or any other purpose the doctor may require. The future possibilities for such a computer are immense, and ultimately it may replace the human doctor almost totally.

The power of the computer can also help the doctor in other ways, for instance, in conjunction with EEG's (Electroencephalographs). EEG's, which have been used for many years in the diagnosis of brain disease, are taken by means of electrical contacts which are made with different parts of the scalp for the purpose of measuring the tiny fluctuations of electrical activity produced by the brain. A diseased brain produces altered electrical fluctuations, and the EEG draws wiggly lines on rolls of paper to give the doctor a record of the brain's electrical activity. Through skill and experience, many doctors can recognise particular abnormal patterns of electrical activity and relate these to specific brain diseases. They can often diagnose brain abscesses, tumours, haemorrhages, or other lesions from the EEG traces, but the task of interpreting such records can be complex. Typically, a patient may have up to sixteen electrodes wired to his scalp, each one linked to a pen which records the electrical activity

Mickie the computer doctor, developed by a group of scientists led by Dr Chris Evans of the National Physical Laboratory (NPL) near London, can interview patients and provide the human doctor with a printed medical history. Tests have shown that patients are more honest and feel more at ease when answering a computer's questions. In the future, it is likely that Mickie will be able to diagnose illnesses and recommend treatments, based on the patient's symptoms. Another NPL invention is Muppet, a computer slightly more bulky than a pocket calculator, which can translate several languages. In the future, it is likely that Muppet will be turned into a portable Mickie – a personal doctor for people who live in remote areas and require diagnostic help, and an aid to doctors in the Third World, where there is a lack of trained personnel and where medical needs are enormous.

on a graph. At the end of the investigation, the doctor may be faced with 50 metres of paper roll with sixteen traces on it, and, obviously there are limits to his ability to recognise abnormalities on such a trace. This is where the computer comes in. At the Royal Free Hospital in London, Professor Bruce McGillivray has programmed a small computer to analyse, record, and compare EEG traces. By storing such records from many different patients, the computer is able to compare thoroughly the different EEG traces and relate different patterns to different brain diseases. The whole process can be done quite automatically, with the resulting interpretation being much more reliable than when done by a doctor.

For many years, the simple X-ray photograph has been the only method of seeing inside the body, but a proliferation of powerful new systems, capable of picturing the inner parts of the body in the minutest detail, is now emerging.

In the space of a few years X-ray scanners have established themselves in the forefront of non-invasive diagnosis. These machines, first produced by the EMI Company in Britain, link a computer to a narrow, moving beam of X-rays which scans the patient's body. As the beam passes through the body at hundreds of different angles, the computer measures its intensity at the other side and builds up a detailed picture of different cross-sections of the body, giving the doctor almost as much information as he could get if he were able to slice the patient up into hundreds of pieces. The X-ray scanner has made it possible to locate the positions and measure the sizes of tumours which could only be seen vaguely on ordinary X-ray photographs. As a result, surgeons can plan their work with higher precision than ever before.

One of the problems of present-day X-ray scanners is that they provide anatomical rather than functional information. It takes many seconds or even minutes to carry out an entire scan, during which time body fluids have travelled considerable distances through the patient. Blood, for example, circulates continuously, and X-ray scanners cannot as yet trace the progress of blood travelling through particular organs for the purpose of checking whether the blood circulation in a particular organ is defective. For this purpose, doctors have recently developed methods of injecting patients with harmlessly radio-active tracer chemicals which, for periods of a few minutes, emit gamma radiation. A device called a gamma camera, which is linked to a television-type screen, measures the intensity of gamma radiation coming from different parts of the body

An experiment in the *artificial eye project* of the University of Utah's Neuroprothesis program. A blind volunteer is shown mapping the position of phosphenes (luminous images on the retina) produced by stimulation of 64 chronically implanted electrodes in contact with the visual cortex of the brain. The computers in the background are used to generate the stimulus and to record the coordinates of the spot touched on the electronically digitised 'blackboard'.

EMI's new series of CT (computerised tomography) scanners make it possible to diagnose illness and plan surgery with higher precision, more speed, and at lower cost than ever before. This is because of the incorporation of microelectronics which provide in one console the manipulation and amplification of data that previously required five separate machines. Whereas traditional scanners require five minutes of X-ray exposure to produce an image on photographic film, with the patient lying still to avoid blurring (affected even by breathing), CT scans can be taken in three to five seconds. Also, whereas conventional X-ray photographs present internal structures superimposed upon each other, CT scans produce, on a television-like screen, a cross-sectional image of the body and can

accurately define small abnormalities in areas as dense as bone. A CT scan, which can yield up to 100 times more information than a conventional X-ray, is produced by an X-ray source and highly sensitive detectors which rotate around the body and can take up to $1\frac{1}{2}$ million readings per scan. These readings, which combine the intensity measurements and geometric coordinates of each beam position, are then processed by the computer and reconstructed in a cross-sectional image. Because each image or 'slice' is quite narrow (about 1 cm, or .4 in) the scan may be repeated in several places to build up a complete picture of the area of interest.

Such machines will vastly improve patient management, enabling doctors to process more patients more quickly, a major

application of such scanners being in the area of cancer treatment. The computer's therapy planning system, which can produce a full treatment plan in seconds, ensures greater accuracy and can aid decisions such as whether to avoid exploratory surgery, increase or decrease radiotherapy, or, if the disease is widespread, whether instead to stop all treatment and improve the quality of the last few months of a patient's life. Future improvements are likely to be three-dimensional X-ray images, now under development, as well as reduction in cost.

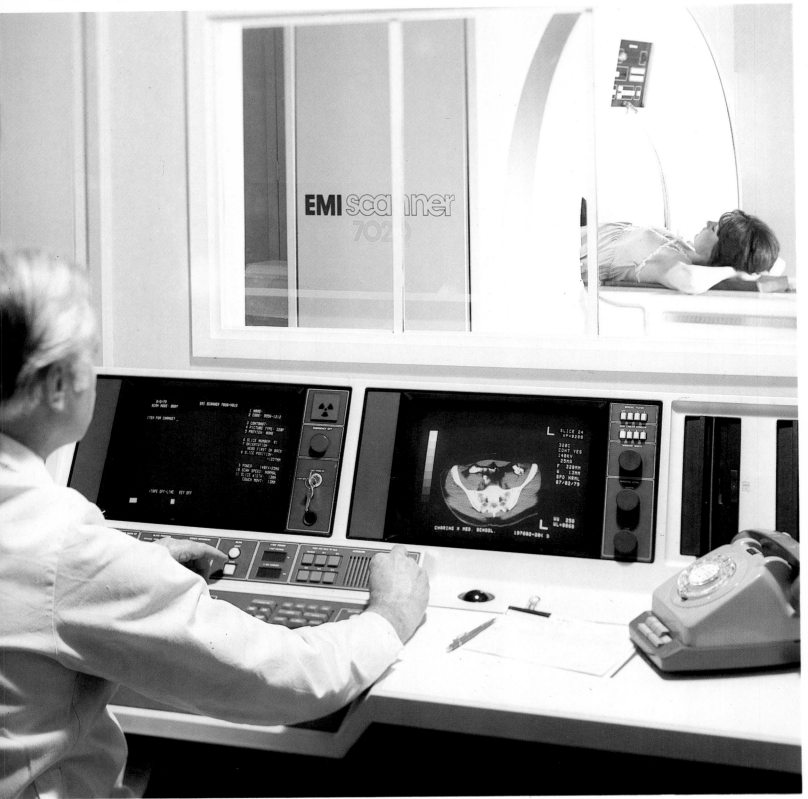

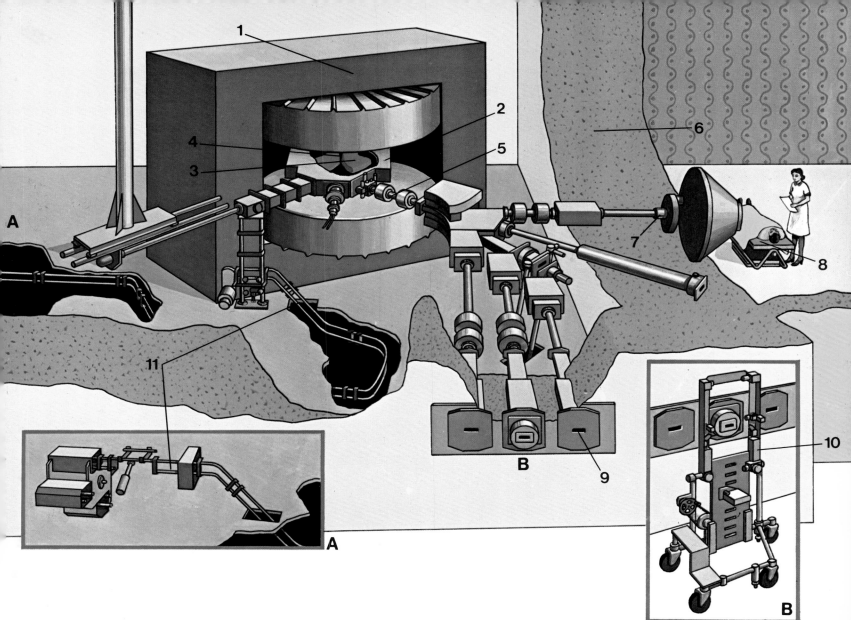

Above

A cyclotron. This machine accelerates atomic particles to very high energies for the purpose of generating radioactive tracer substances which are passed into the patient's body. These are then recorded by a gamma camera which measures the intensities of radiation emitted from various parts of the body and can help doctors locate abnormalities such as tumours. The tracer substances emit radiation for very short periods of time and thus pose no long-term hazard to the patient. (1) Cyclotron electromagnet. (2) Vacuum acceleration chamber. (3) Accelerating electrodes 'Dees'. (4) Ion source. (5) Charged particle beam channel. (6) Concrete walls 2 m (6.6 ft) thick for radiation shielding. (7) Neutron-forming target of Beryllium. (8) Neutron therapy treatment couch. (9) Beam ports for targets for radionuclide production. (10) Multiple target assembly for remote control. (11) Remotely controlled railway for target transport to processing laboratory.

Right

A gamma camera scan of the chest.

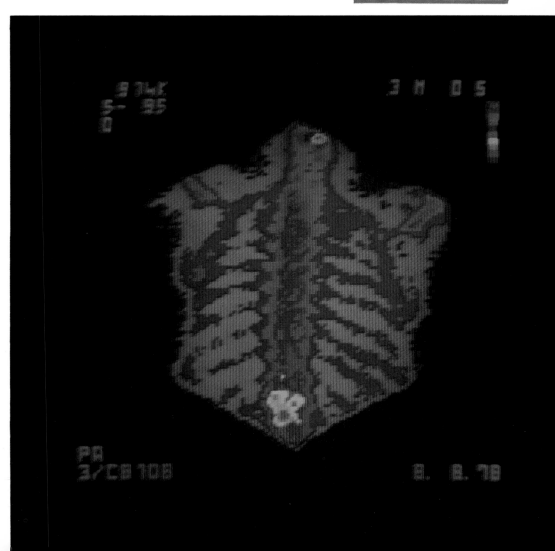

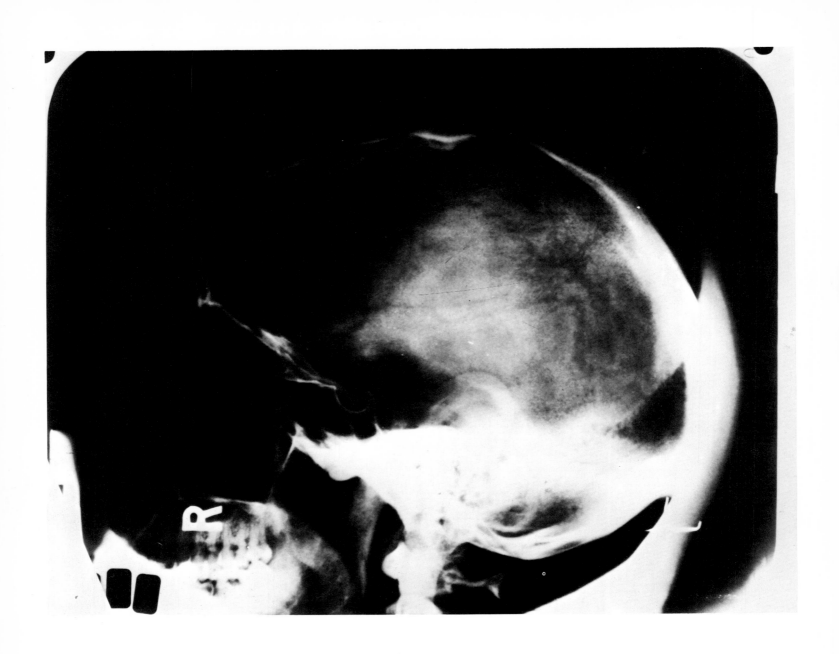

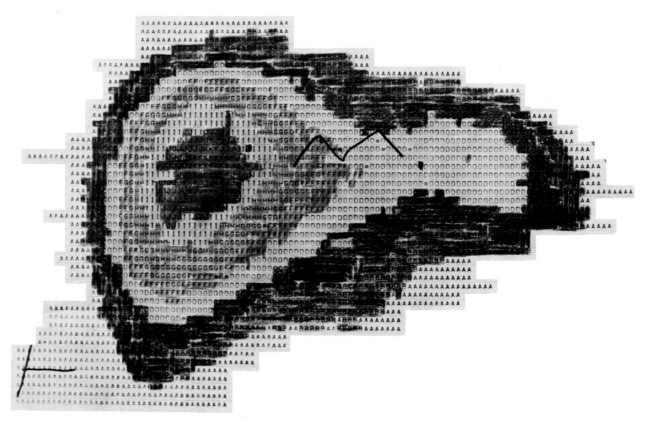

138

where the tracer chemical has penetrated, and photographs the pattern of chemical's progress through the body. A similar system, which has been used successfully by doctors at the Hammersmith Hospital in London, is carried out by a machine called a cyclotron, which accelerates atomic particles to very high energies for the purpose of generating tracer substances which remain radioactive for very short periods of time only, and thus pose no long-term radiation hazard to the patient. Dr Anthony Pinching at Hammersmith has been using a radio-active isotope of oxygen produced by the cyclotron. His patients inhale the isotope along with ordinary air, and as it penetrates different parts of the brain, it can easily be seen through the gamma camera. These methods open up the possibility of observing a wide range of natural processes in progress within the body. By measuring the speed at which different biological processes take place in their patients, doctors in the future may be able to investigate illnesses and understand them more thoroughly than ever before. What may be more important they will be able to watch the effects of different medications as they are used on the patients and intervene immediately if things go wrong. New techniques like this promise to make the human body increasingly 'transparent' to doctors in the future.

A completely different method of scanning, called nuclear magnetic resonance scanning, which was developed at Nottingham University in England by Dr Waldo Hinshaw and his colleagues, and announced at the beginning of 1978, has already been taken up by commercial interests. In this system, which has important advantages over isotopes and X-rays, a beam of high-frequency radio waves is directed into the patient. Normally it would pass right through, hardly being absorbed at all, but by means of a system of electro-magnets which are focussed onto the specific parts of the body required for examination, the body tissues are transformed from being transparent to being partially opaque. Whereas X-rays are absorbed mostly in hard tissues such as bone, the radio waves are absorbed in soft body tissues, the pattern of absorption being related to the amount of water and certain other chemicals held within each part of the organ, making them ideal for locating such abnormalities as tumours. Because the living cells of the body absorb radio waves only when the electro-magnets are focussed on them, the radio waves can be used like X-ray beams to perform scanning. By using computers to alter the point at which the magnetism is concentrated on the body, this new diagnostic

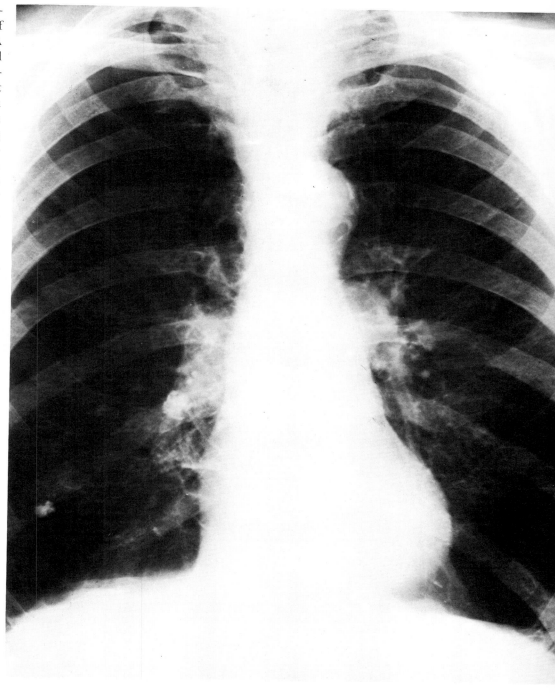

tool can be made to examine one region within the body after another, the rest of the body, not under the influence of magnetism, remaining transparent to the radio waves. This new scanning technique is called nuclear magnetic resonance scanning because it depends on the absorption of radio radiation within the nuclei of atoms under the influence of magnetism. It has also been given the slightly shorter name of zeugmatography. Only initial research work has been done so far, but zeugmatography looks very promising because of its capacity to reveal conditions which could be missed with X-rays. Also, it is thought that exposure of the body to high frequency radio waves is quite harmless, unlike X-rays which cause a slight radiation hazard.

The use of ultrasound is another method that is likely to be used increasingly in the years ahead for a wide range

Above
Conventional X-ray of clavicle (collar bone), ribs, lungs, and heart.

Opposite top
Conventional X-ray of a scull. No soft tissue is visible.

Opposite below
This complex diagram, produced by a computer from information about a patient's measurements and X-ray results, gives exact information on the course of treatment required. In the case of cancer, the information would include the intensity, duration, and angle of radiation treatment required.

of non-invasive investigations. Basically, ultrasound is no different from audible sound. Its pitch is higher, beyond the range of the human ear, but, as with sound, it consists of waves of compression and rarification in the air, in solids, or in liquids. The human body transmits ultrasound very well, but different organs within the body have different physical properties such as density and elasticity. Because of this, an ultrasonic wave is partially reflected every time it passes from one organ to another on its way through the body. Thus, beams of ultrasound directed into the body have been found to be particularly useful in locating bounderies of different kinds of tissues. This is one reason that ultrasound equipment has been ideal for viewing the growing foetus in the womb and for locating tumours. Another reason is that so far ultrasound has not been found to pose any danger, to either patient or doctor. Although ultrasound equipment is already in wide-

spread use, after only a few years since it was initially developed, the scope for using it more widely in the future is immense. To begin with, it can reveal parts of the body which other scanning techniques cannot, and should thus become part of the doctor's comprehensive armoury of different diagnostic tools.

As with all the new diagnostic tools, different methods of using ultrasound are continually being developed. At the Institute of Cancer Research, in Sutton, near London, Dr David Nicholas has developed a method called ultrasonic diffraction scanning. This makes it possible to probe within organs and tumours and show up much of their internal structure. The principle of the method is similar to the technique of X-ray crystallography which scientists have been using for many years to examine the shapes of complex biological molecules. In the case of ultrasound diffraction, the ultrasound beam is directed into the

patient in the normal way, but instead of looking for obvious boundaries within the body, the doctors look for diffraction patterns which arise from a combination of hundreds of tiny reflections of ultrasound coming from within the organ or tumour being examined. The Sutton team has been able to distinguish between malignant and benign tumours by examining this pattern. When the system is computerised, it should be possible to produce on a television screen an actual picture of the internal structure of the organ so that doctors will be able to view not only the external shape and position of a tumour, but its internal structure.

Yet another refinement of ultrasound diagnosis, which may be able to help detect breast cancer at very early stages, has been developed by Dr Peter Wells at the Bristol General Hospital, in the West of England. A growing tumour requires more blood than the normal healthy breast tissue. Dr Wells' method of investigation, which involves aiming a

140

beam of ultrasound into the breast, works by detecting areas where the blood is flowing faster than usual. This is possible because the pitch of a beam of ultrasound is altered by travelling in flowing blood, or any other moving fluid. This alteration, known as Doppler Effect, is also what happens when an ambulance or police car passes with its siren sounding, the siren seeming to alter in pitch as the vehicle passes.

Despite all of these new techniques, the tremendous diagnostic powers of future doctors may still be defeated because there are very few major diseases for which vastly improved treatment or cure is clearly anticipated. Indeed the two biggest killer diseases of modern times: cancer and heart disease, are on the increase, and their causes and patterns of development within the body are so complex that most physicians expect no more than a gradual improve-

ment in treatments during the coming decades. Mental illness is also on the increase, and the two most common of these, schizophrenia and depression, are little nearer to being understood today than they were many years ago. A real hope for the future is that some of the underlying biochemical causes of these conditions might be discovered. This could lead to effective treatments and cures, but although drugs have been developed which effectively control many of the symptoms, the prospects for discovering new psycho-active drugs to cure schizophrenia and depression seem rather gloomy at present. So what hopes can realistically be held out for the future of medical treatments?

Dr Lewis Thomas, President of the Memorial Sloane Kettering Cancer Center in New York, one of the leading centres for cancer research and treatment in the world, believes that the main hope for

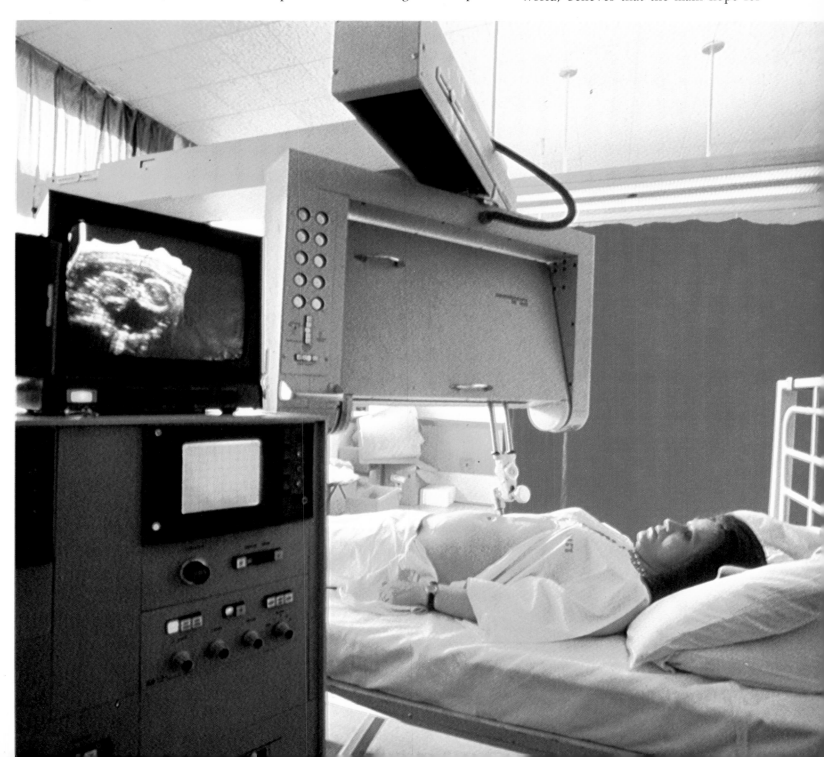

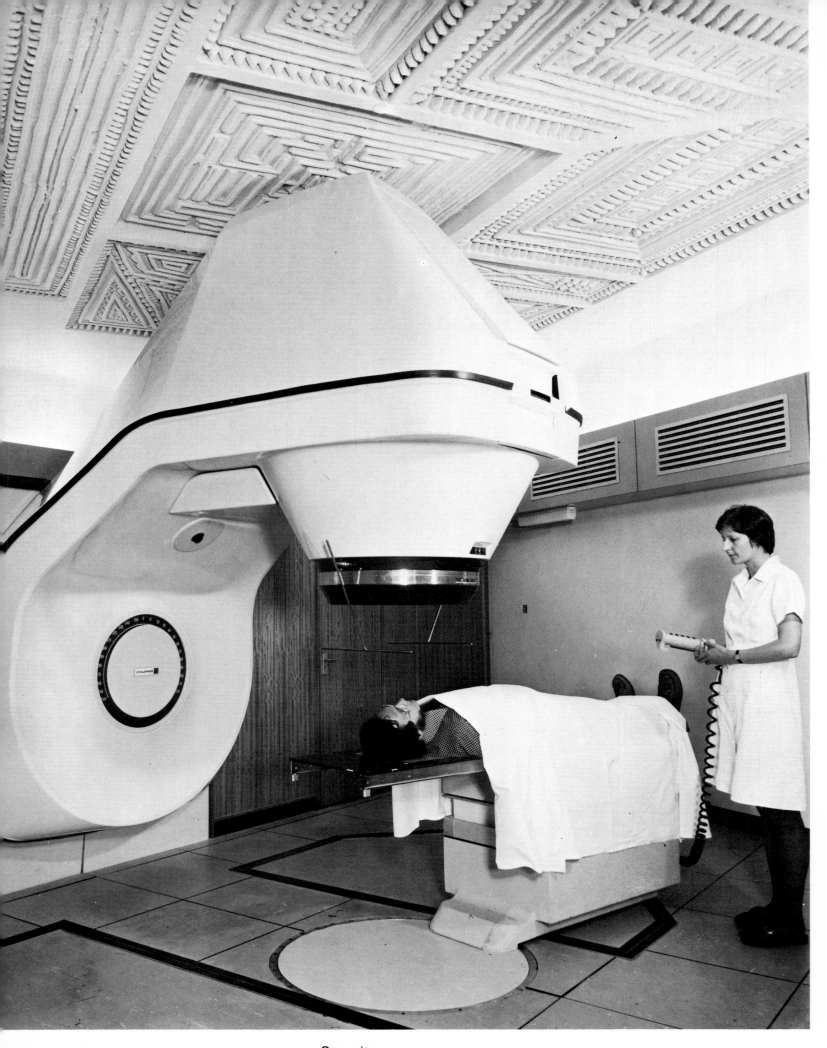

A patient being set up for treatment with fast neutrons, using the adjustable head of the Medical Research Council's Cyclotron at the Western General Hospital in Edinburgh.

Opposite

The *gamma camera* is used in conjunction with a cyclotron to measure the intensity of gamma radiation radio-active tracer substances which have penetrated

different parts of the body. Linked to a television-like screen, the gamma camera photographs the chemical's pattern of progress through the body.

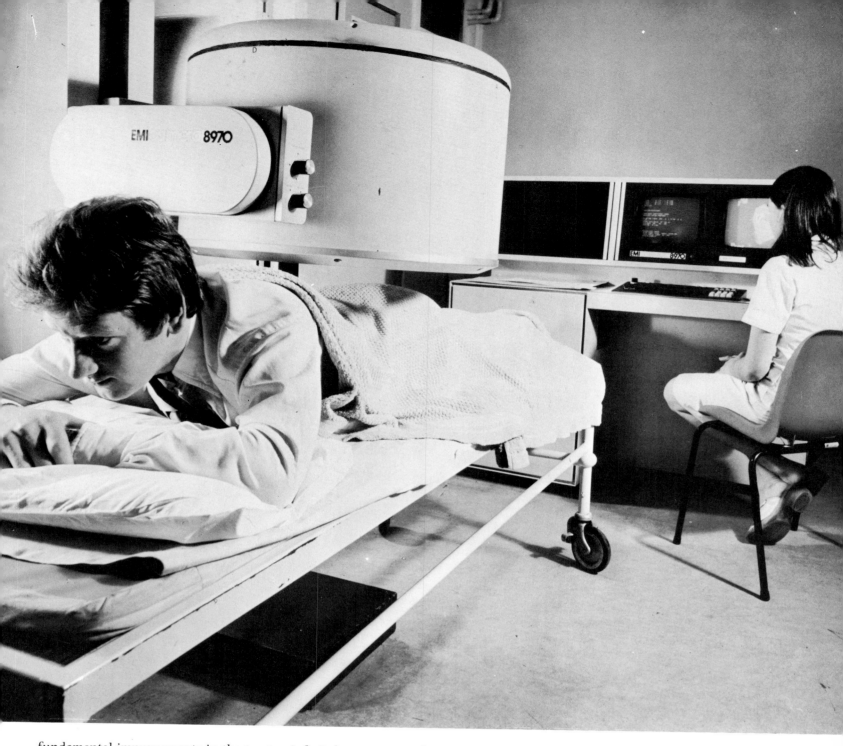

fundamental improvements in the treatment of cancer and other diseases lies in man's increasing understanding of the basic science of the human body. Up until now doctors have been able to gain little benefit from basic scientific research of living cells because there has been such a huge gap between the level of complexity encountered in a human being who is ill, and the bacterium, the enormously simpler organism which the scientists are beginning to understand. The molecular structure of the genes is quite well understood now, thanks to techniques such as X-ray crystallography which gave scientists the means of locating individual atoms within quite complex biological molecules. Current research is beginning to show which pieces of the genetic blueprint molecule, DNA, are responsible for particular characteristics of the complete organism. This is a long way from understanding the almost

infinitely more complex human being, but progress in this fundamental research is quite rapid. When this gap in understanding has closed, doctors will be able to get medical advice primarily from scientists who will have achieved a genuine understanding of bodily mechanisms, right down to the level of individual atoms within the living cells from which the body is constructed. At such a time, the whole of medicine will be turned upside down.

Great steps forward may also be made in preventive medicine. In the past, many of the infectious diseases have yielded to vaccination and to the development of antibiotics which can fight infections caused by bacteria. Certainly, more vaccines may be developed in the future.

A vaccine against the disease known as Type–B hepatitis which poses a great danger to people receiving blood trans-

fusions is currently being developed. This disease is widespread in parts of Africa and is thought to be a cause of liver cancer. Dr Alfred Prince at the New York Blood Bank and other scientists in the United States and in Liberia have now developed the vaccine to the point of testing it in humans.

Another serious infection likely to undergo vaccination programmes is venereal disease. Many experts now believe that it will soon be possible to prepare vaccines against gonorrhoea and syphilis. Many doctors also believe that most forms of cancer are preventable. Lung cancer is the prime example. Most cases are caused by tobacco smoking, so the simple step of persuading people to stop smoking would almost eliminate the disease. And scientific research may be able to develop safe substitutes for commonly abused substances such as alcohol and tobacco. Scientists are al-

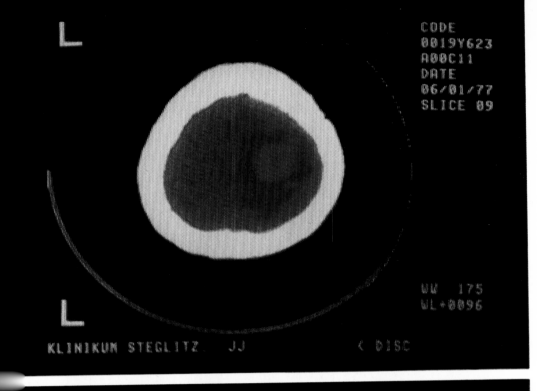

CT scan of a cross-section of the brain, showing clearly details of the brain tissue. There is an abnormality in the right side of the brain.

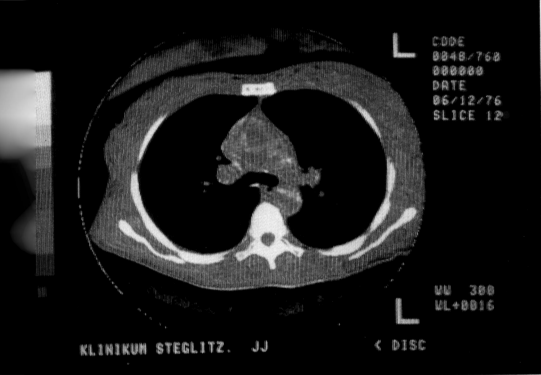

CT scan of the heart.

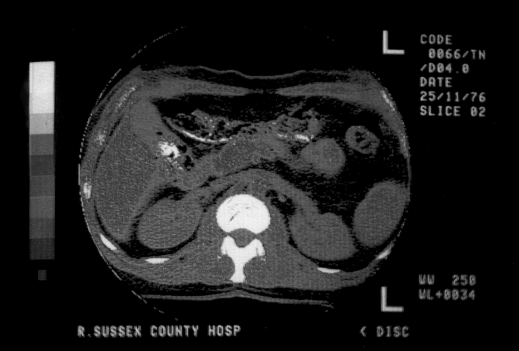

CT scan of the liver, spleen, vertebra, and kidneys.

ready developing foods with little nutritive value which could help overcome the problem of over-eating, something thought to contribute to such illnesses as heart disease, diabetes and hypertension. Drugs may even be developed to effectively reduce appetite without bringing about side-effects. Also, some sense may eventually be made of the complex pattern of the disease-causing effects of different diets. At present, there are many conflicting reports about whether certain foods tend to produce particular diseases or not and many detailed trials of foods and studies of the geographical distribution of diseases, are in progress. It is quite possible that within a few years doctors may be able to recommend patterns of diet with confidence, having reached definite conclusions about the health hazards of different foods.

Birth control has also been an important area of medical progress recently, and it is widely predicted that the so-called Morning After Pill, which could be taken after sexual intercourse to prevent the implantation of any fertilised embryo, will be available within one or two decades. The great advantage of this pill is that, unlike present-day pills, women would not need to take it every day, thus removing any long term risks which may be associated with ordinary contraceptive pills. Yet another approach which already looks very promising is the contraceptive pill for men.

Possibly the biggest single medical breakthrough of the twentieth century was the discovery of antibiotics, chemical agents which can kill infectious bacteria without harming the patient. An important hope for the future is that virus illnesses may also eventually be cured by drugs.

Viruses are the simplest forms of life. To live and reproduce they have to stay within a living cell. The main problem with producing anti-viral drugs in the past has been that any agent which attacked the virus would also tend to harm the human cell in which the virus lives.

It is ironical that in the present age of technical sophistication we are not able to cure such common illnesses as influenza and colds, but research indicates that such cures may soon be in sight. Anti-viral agents to combat the herpes virus, which causes cold sores and other problems, have already been developed in the form of ointments which can be applied to the skin, but no anti-viral drug which can be taken orally has been produced. This may soon change, however, thanks to research at the Wellcome Laboratories in Beckenham, near London, and at their sister research establishment in North Carolina in the United States.

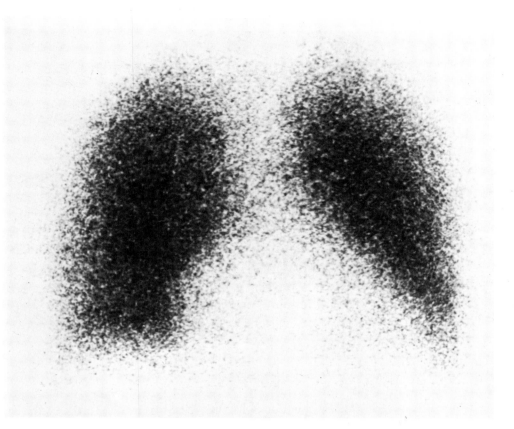

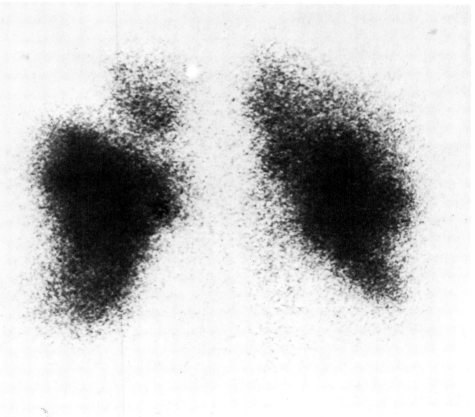

Top: Photograph from a cyclotron scan of normally ventrilated (air flow) lungs.
Above: A scan of the same lungs, using a different isotope, shows an abnormal perfusion (blood flow). The difference between the two scans allows the physician to make the diagnosis of pulmonary embolism, a condition which causes 140,000 deaths and affects a further 560,000 people a year in the U.S.A.

The growing sophistication of medical science has led to considerable advances in the diagnosis and treatment of disease. Here the patient is being scanned by a CT (computerized tomography) unit which produces an extremely accurate X-ray analysis. By recording a number of cross-sections of the area under examination a three dimensional image of the patient's internal structure can be obtained. The computer can then produce an almost immediate treatment plan to assist the doctor in deciding what action to take, and links to external data banks will allow access to the full range of specialist information.

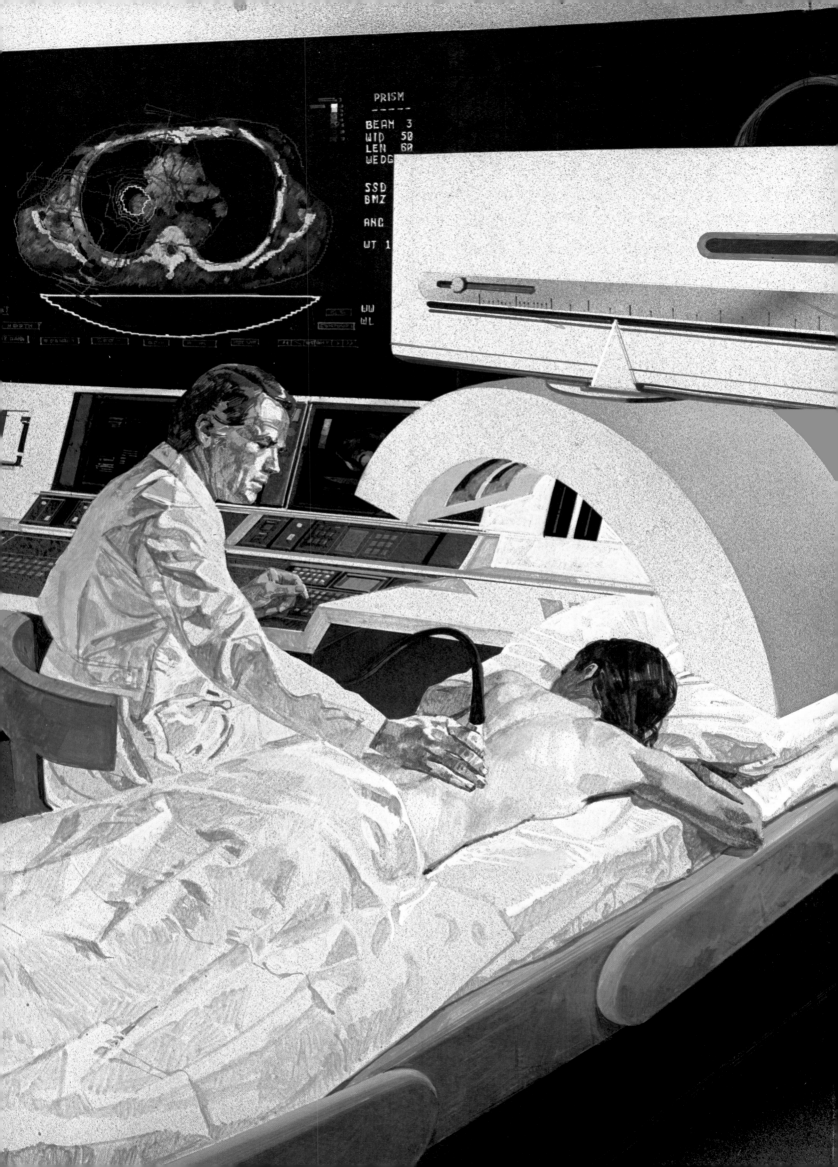

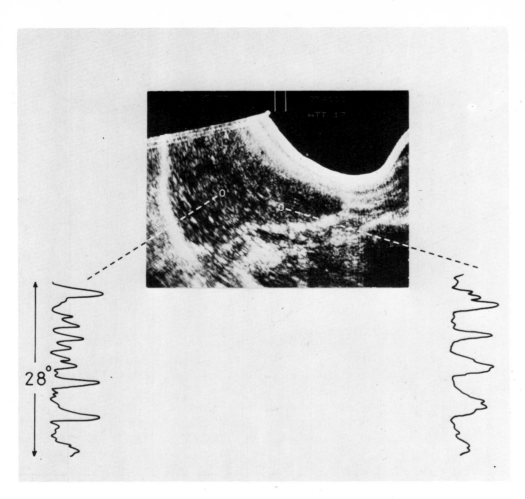

Ultrasound scanning techniques, which can accurately locate the boundaries and determine densities of different tissues within the body, are especially useful for viewing a growing foetus in the womb or for locating tumours. The two different diffraction patterns shown come from (left) a metastatic deposit in the liver and (right) normal liver tissue.

This British and American team has now discovered a drug which attacks a part of the virus's molecular machinery which is completely different from any molecules possessed by the host cell. Because of this, it has proved possible to kill the virus without affecting the cell. The Wellcome scientists' drug, which fights the herpes virus, has been tested on animals, and research leader Dr John Bauer at Beckenham believes that it may lead to a drug which can be taken orally by humans to cure illnesses caused by herpes and viruses similar to it. If the work fulfills its promise, there is a hope that more chemical agents will be discovered or synthesised which can attack the virus's weak points in this way.

At present, scientists have little understanding of why particular chemical molecules have specific effects on the human body and upon disease-producing organisms. Because of this, a great deal of skillful guesswork has to go into designing new drug molecules, and when a promising one is developed, it has to be tested in the test tube, then on animals, and finally on humans, the whole process lasting up to ten years or in some cases even longer. There is hope that disease theories and the chemistry of drugs may be understood well enough to develop safe, effective agents without so much tedious work using trial and error procedures, but until then existing, well-known drugs could potentially be used more effectively. Steroids, for example,

are known to be effective in the treatment of rheumatoid arthritis, but doctors found that side effects of steroid treatment made it unsafe for most patients. Rheumatoid arthritis is mainly confined to joints, which become swollen and painful. What is needed if steroids are to be used again is a method of delivering a high dose of the drug to the diseased joint, and a much lower amount to the rest of the body where side effects could exert themselves. At the Strangeways Laboratory in Cambridge, England, Dr John Dingle and colleagues are attempting to solve this problem by delivering the drug directly to the joints in tiny oil droplets. The droplets, which are called liposomes, consist of concentric shells of oil, with the active drug molecules sandwiched between each shell. The liposomes are absorbed into the lubricating synovial fluid of the joint and are too big to escape into the rest of the body. Thus, very high doses of steroids are delivered to the joints and very little goes elsewhere. The hope is that by treating only the target area, the problem of dangerous side effects will be overcome. There is still no known cure for rheumatoid arthritis, but such a treatment may reduce or eliminate the symptoms.

One of the problems facing the doctor who wants to keep a close watch on his patient's progress is that tests made in the surgery may produce misleading results. To begin with, a single test such as the patient's blood pressure gives the doctor

only one single reading and he will not know whether the blood pressure was different at different times of the day. Also, if the patient is apprehensive about coming to see the doctor, his blood pressure may rise in response to his fear even if there is nothing wrong with him.

To solve this, doctors are beginning to monitor their patients by remote control systems such as the one developed by Dr F. D. Stott at the Clinical Research Centre of Northwick Park Hospital, near London. In this system, tiny contact devices fitted to the patient feed measurements directly into a tape recorder for up to twenty-four hours at a time. Miniature tape recorders can record blood pressure, electrical activity of the brain, heart beat, and potentially many other factors while the patient is carrying on his normal life. The tape is later replayed and analysed by computer to spot any unexpected variations or abnormalities. For example, such systems make it possible to pick out the few abnormal heart beats which may occur among the 100,000 or so beats taking place every day. In one series of trials of this new method, called ambulatory monitoring, five times as many medical problems were spotted in a group of patients with the help of the tape recordings than were detected by ordinary medical examinations. The doctors were able to conduct continuous twenty-four hour surveillance of their patients without having to use expensive hospital facilities.

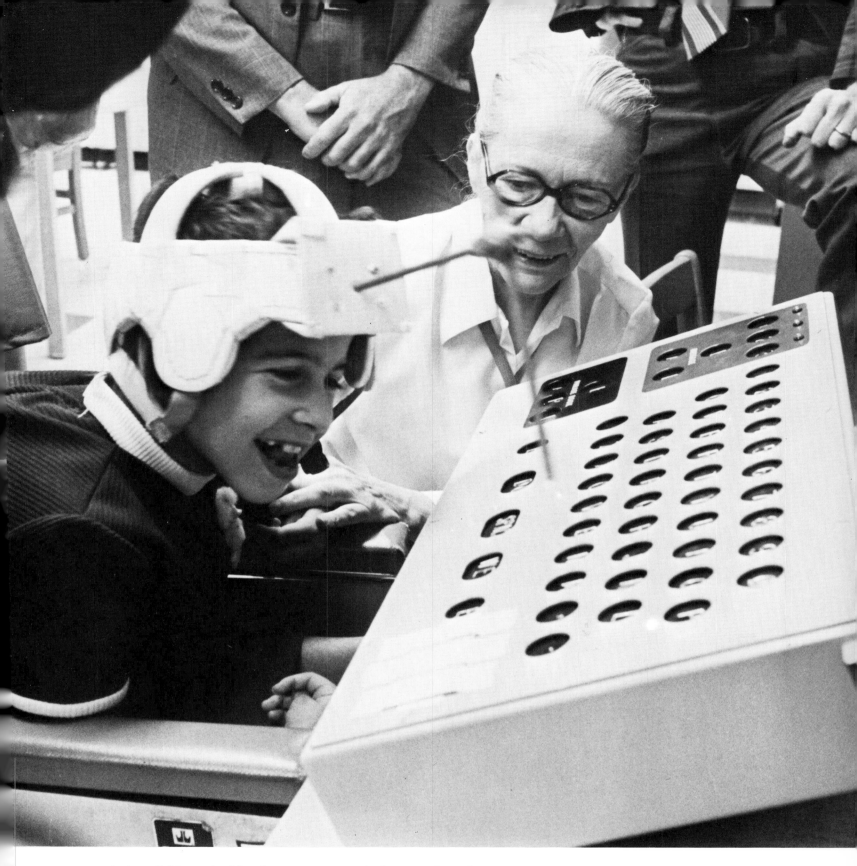

One variation of this method has been developed at the Royal Victoria Infirmary in Newcastle upon Tyne, England, by engineer John Osselton. His system involves linking electroencephalograph electrodes to a tiny radio transmitter strapped to the patent's wrist. Brainwaves can thus be sent by radio over distances of up to half a kilometre where they can be recorded and analysed by computer to check for signs of epilepsy during the patient's normal life. Another adaptation has been developed in Scotland by Dr James McGregor of the University of Strathclyde. He has developed a device called LAPSE (Long-term Ambulatory Physiological Surveillance Equipment), a heart-monitoring system which consists of a tape recorder mounted on the patient's hip and electrical contacts mounted on the chest. The tape recorder also has contact with a crystal clock to record the time at regular intervals on the tape, as well as connections to accelerometers on the patient's body which register his body positions (standing, sitting, lying down and so on). When the tape is replayed, the doctors are able to see how the heart activity varied at different times of the day and in response to different body positions. LAPSE, and devices like it, could

Using this oversized, portable keyboard, the disabled can compose messages by touching a button with a finger or a pointer fastened to a head cap. The keyboard is connected to a microcomputer which is also connected to a TV set and page printer. To reduce the amount of typing, the microcomputer automatically types out abbreviations for words, word endings, and phrases. A cerebral palsied child uses a pointer fixed to a headcap to type a message on the keyboard of an experimental Computer Assisted Communications System.

Recent developments in tape recording technology have made it feasible to acquire and store data on an unconfined patient for periods of twenty-four hours or more. At the core of the *ambulatory monitoring system* are 4-channel sub-miniature tape recorders such as the one pictured, designed by D.F.D. Scott of the Bio-engineering Division of the Clinical Research Centre, and now being produced by Oxford Electronic Instruments Limited. These can record and monitor blood pressure or heartbeats using a conventional cassette tape that is run at a lower than normal speed. Examination and interpretation of the collected data is carried out by largely automatic equipment which can recognise abnormalities and transcribe these for subsequent examination, by means of a conventional pen-recorder. It is hoped that in the future, such interpretation will be facilitated by more advanced computer technologies.

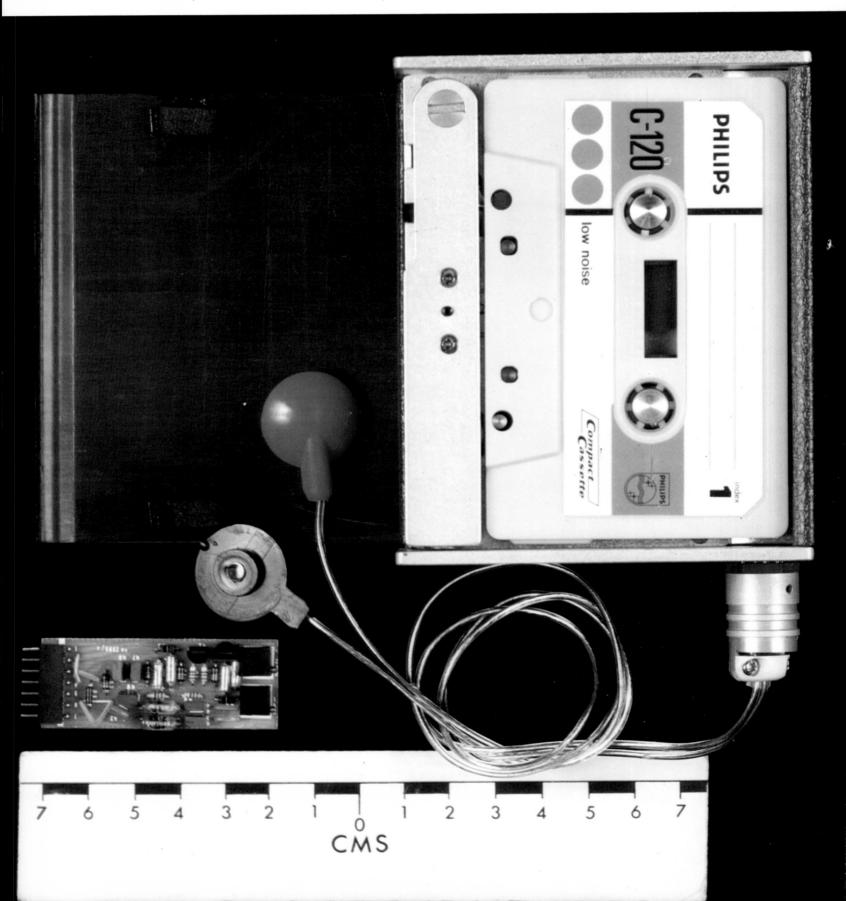

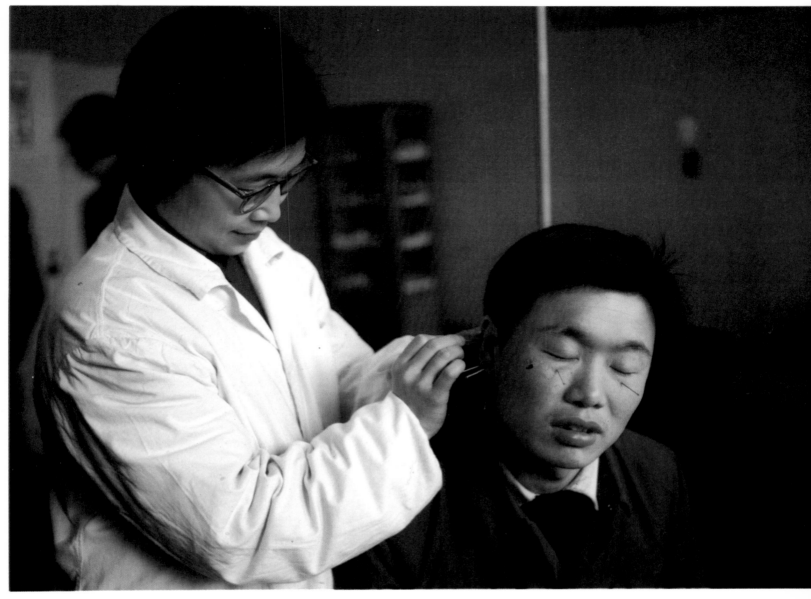

Acupuncture, here being performed for the treatment of short sight at the Wuhan Hospital in China, has contributed greatly to the discovery and understanding of the body's natural pain-killing substances. Scientists believe that it may one day be possible to manipulate these substances to relieve pain.

easily be developed to record any number of situations which the doctor considers are significant, such as recovering from an operation, or learning to cope with an artificial limb. Because of this combination of effectiveness and potential savings in terms of medical resources, hospitals of the future may well have departments of ambulatory monitoring along with all the other familiar (and some not so familiar) departments such as pathology, X-ray, ultrasound diagnosis, and so on.

The end of the twentieth century may see the development of an artificial ear for totally deaf people whose auditory nerves still function. The very beginnings of this technology have already been achieved at the University of Cambridge, where Dr Brian Moore of the Department of Psychology, working with colleagues from London University and Guy's Hospital in London, has developed a crude form of artificial ear which restores a wisp of hearing to the totally deaf. It consists of an electrical contact wired directly to the auditory nerve as well as to a microphone that picks up voice sounds. With it, the deaf

person hears only a buzzing noise – the voice of a person he is listening to. It is impossible to make out individual words with the present system, but intonation can sometimes be detected, helping to distinguish between questions, statements and so on, and it is possible to distinguish between certain vowels. Because of this, the present, crude experimental device has already proved useful as an aid to lip reading. In the future, it may be possible to attach several different electrical contacts to the auditory nerve. Connected to microphones, these could register different audible frequencies so that the deaf person could begin to hear a more complete spectrum of sounds. If such systems work well, the number of electrical contacts could be increased until a deaf person could hear almost normally. Even in its present simple form, however, the artificial ear helps eliminate the feeling of total isolation.

In the future, life should also be a great deal more enjoyable for partially deaf people. Up until now, most deaf aids have been designed merely to amplify sounds, despite the fact that deaf people often

151

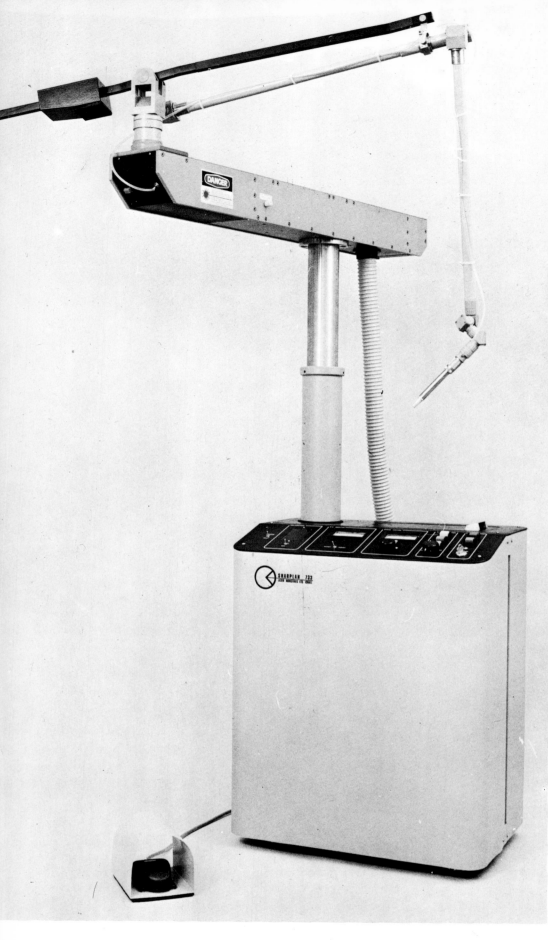

The Sharplan 733 is one of the few *surgical laser units* presently available commercially. Still in its infancy, laser surgery promises to revolutionize certain kinds of operations, especially those on cancerous tumours. Although surgical incisions made with lasers take longer than with an ordinary scalpel, they have the advantage that some of the blood vessels around the cut are immediately sealed, reducing bleeding and thereby stopping the spread of infection or of cancer cells to the surrounding tissue.

Another benefit of this technology is that because lasers can be manipulated to follow any path, microsurgery can be performed with greater precision by directing the beam through light guides or pipes.

hear some audible frequences better than others. High pitched notes, for example, may not be heard well by a patient who may hear low-pitched notes quite easily. This problem may not be neglected for very much longer. Electronic devices, constructed from cheap, miniature components, should soon make it possible for deaf aids to be constructed with amplifiers that enhance only those audible frequencies which the deaf person needs to hear louder. Each deaf person could be tested in a studio over a wide range of sound frequencies, giving the doctor a precise profile of his patient's hearing ability. The profile could then be fed directly into a computer so that the deaf aid could be adjusted and programmed automatically to suit the patient's hearing needs.

The control of pain is also likely to improve greatly in the future as a result of several quite distinct research achievements. An explanation for the pain-killing effects of the Chinese practice of acupuncture was advanced recently following the discovery of natural pain-killing substances, the enkephalins, found to be present in the body. These substances were first isolated from pigs' brains by Dr J. Hughes and his colleagues in Aberdeen, Scotland. Since then, Professor Michael Besser and colleagues at St Bartholomews Hospital in London have measured the concentrations of enkephalins in humans. Professor Besser believes that it may be possible to manipulate these substances, which have been called the brain's natural opiates, to relieve pain. A different approach to pain control, developed by Dr Blane Marshall of the Duke Medical Center in North Carolina and adopted by the doctors there, is a method which involves intercepting the nerve impulses which transmit the sensation of pain from a diseased part of the body to the brain. In this system, a tiny radio receiver is implanted into the patient's back and connected to his spinal cord (up which the pain messages have to travel in order to reach the brain) and the patient carries a small radio transmitter strapped around his waist. When the patient feels pain, he operates the transitter so that a radio signal is sent to the tiny implanted receiver. This in turn transmits an electrical signal into the spinal cord. The signal blocks the nerve impulse which would normally transmit the sensation of pain to the brain.

Pain control is also likely to be the central feature of a new approach to dying. At certain specialist centres, doctors and nurses are now treating terminally ill patients in the sure knowledge that their lives will not be prolonged. Instead, the emphasis is on giving the patients a quality of life in their last days which is as good as possible under the circumstances. This trend was pioneered by Dr Cicely Saunders at the Saint Christopher's Hospice near London. The concept of the hospice, a place where doctors concentrate on the treatment of pain, particularly in terminally ill patients, has now caught on. Many other units have now been set up in Britain, and some also in the United States. It has been found that by carefully using the well-known methods of pain control, most patients can lead a pain-free and almost normal life right up to the point of death. At a hospice, doctors use a full armoury of pain-killing drugs, from the familiar aspirin to the sometimes feared heroin. In the past, many doctors have been reluctant to prescribe heroin until the very last moments in the patient's life. In medical school, they were trained to believe that the problems of tolerance and addiction to this drug could easily bring more harm than good. However, hospice physicians have discovered that when heroin is properly used under the supervision of a doctor, and taken by mouth, neither tolerance nor addiction occur. They also find that patients do not have an altered state of mind. They are relieved of their pain, but experience very few other effects except occasional nausea and constipation, both of which can be removed by other drugs. In the hospice, medical staff pay detailed attention to each of the many sources of pain and discomfort which patients report. Infection may be a source of pain often overlooked in terminally ill patients, and can be treated by antibiotics rather than pain-killing drugs. Psychological worries, which may cause more concern than the pain of disease, are also attended to. The result is that many patients spend their last days productively: attending to their family business, seeing friends, and taking holidays before they die, instead of suffering slowly as has been common in the past.

As the world gets richer, the need for new types of medical care such as the hospice increases because life is increasingly prolonged, and people die not from the swift blow of an infectious disease, but from the remaining killers such as cancer, heart disease, and the ailments of old age.

However, the quest to prolong life is likely to become increasingly sophisticated and successful in the years ahead. The transplanting of live human organs may become even more reliable than it is today, although most experts admit that the problems of tissue rejection, leading to the failure of the transplanted organ as time goes by, are likely to remain daunting. On the other hand, the bionic man, familiar to television viewers and science fiction readers, may soon become a reality. In the United States, scientists at the University of Utah in Salt Lake City have developed a whole range of artificial organs which seem poised for human use, among them an artificial arm, developed by Dr Stephen Jacobsen, which mimics many of the abilities of a real arm. The 'Utah arm' is fitted to the stump and connected electrically to the patient's nervous system. Nerve impulses are fed into a tiny computer built into the arm which controls every movement. As yet, the 'Utah arm' does not have the strength of an ordinary arm, and so cannot be used for heavy work, but new engineering techniques, and the discovery of a means of connecting it rigidly to the remaining bone in the patient's stump, could eventually give the prosthesis almost all of the qualities of a normal arm.

The University of Utah team is also developing artificial hearts which can be implanted into the body; a portable kidney machine which can be strapped to the patient's waist; an artificial eye; systems of restoring hearing to the totally deaf, similar in some ways to the methods of Dr Moore in Cambridge, England; and plastic replacements for blood vessels, nerves, bile ducts and a range of other organs. In England, a partially bionic pancreas was developed recently by Dr Norman Lazarus and Mr Ronald Gates at the Wellcome Foundation Laboratories near London. In experiments, the doctors have transplanted pancreatic tissue from rabbits into rats. Normally such an operation would fail because of tissue rejection, but the Wellcome team have developed a special plastic membrane, called a nucleopore membrane, which encapsulates the rabbit pancreas. Nutrients from the rat's body can pass into the transplanted pancreas to keep it alive, but white blood cells, which are responsible for tissue rejection, cannot. The result is that the pancreas can continue to function normally and provide insulin for its unfamiliar host. If such transplants can be performed in humans, there is hope that the 'bionic pancreas' could effectively cure diabetes.

If developments such as these continue – and there is no reason why they shouldn't – our future world should be almost unrecognisable in the terms on which we see it today.

Index

References to illustrations are in italics

In some cases where a word appears frequently in the text, reference is only given for the page on which it is defined.

ACKNOWLEDGEMENTS LIST

p.10: Ferranti Ltd., p.11: Bell Laboratories, U.S.A.; p.12 *top*: Topix; p.12 *bottom*: Ferranti Ltd; p.13: I.B.M.; p.14 *top*: Bell Laboratories; p.14 *bottom*: EMI Threshold Ltd.; p.15: Menzies Communications Systems; p.16: *Practical Computing*; p.17 *top*: *Daily Telegraph* Colour Library (photo: Martin Goddard); p.17 *bottom*: Phillips Industries (Photo: Beaver Publications); p.18: Transport and Road Research Laboratory; p.19: Bell Laboratories; p.22: American Telephone and Telegraph Company; p.23: Syndication International; p.24 *top*: Personal Computers Ltd; p.24 *bottom*: Alternative Energy Group, Hull College; p.26: Camera Press (photo: Ralph Crane); p.27: Camera Press; p.28: Bell Laboratories; p.29: Monotype International; p.30: Data Dynamics; p.31: Camera Press (Photo: Bill Snyder); p.32 *top*: Bell Laboratories; p.32 *bottom*: European Space Agency (E.S.A.); p.33 *top*: Bell Laboratories; p.33 *bottom*: British Aerospace; p.34: Comsat Laboratories, U.S.A.; p.35: Comsat Laboratories; p.38: British Aerospace; p.39: Jodrell Bank; p.40: Arthur C. Clarke; p.41: Space Frontiers Ltd; p.43: U.K. Atomic Energy Authority (U.K.A.E.A.); p.44: Jeff Becker, U.S.A; p.45 *top* and *bottom*: Jeff Becker, U.S.A.; p.46: U.K.A.E.A.; p.47 *top*: Lewis Research Centre, U.S.A.; p.47 *bottom*: Sandia Laboratories, U.S.A.; p.48 *top* and *bottom*: U.K.A.E.A.; p.50: Queens University, Belfast; p.51: U.K.A.E.A; p.52: Wavepower Ltd; p.53: Information Office, French Embassy; p.54: Central Electricity Generating Board; p.55 *top* and *bottom*: Department of Energy, U.S.A.; p.58 *top*: Department of Energy, U.S.A.; p.58 *bottom*: Institute of Energy Conversion, U.S.A.; p.59: Information Service, French Embassy; p.60: MIT Lincoln Laboratory, U.S.A.; p.61: MIT Lincoln Laboratory, U.S.A.; p.62: Pacific Gas and Electric Company, U.S.A.; p.63: Camera Press (photo: Gerard Schachmes); p.66: Los Alamos Scientific Laboratory, U.S.A.; p.67: Professor M.W. Thring, Queen Mary College, London; p.69: Covell, Matthews, Wheatley and Partners Ltd; p.71 *top*: A. Bolandi, Department of Mechanical Engineering, Queen Mary College, London; p.71 *bottom*: Lucas Electric; p.74: G.E.S., West Germany; p.75 *top*: Pats-centre International; p.75 *bottom*: Professor B.V. Jayawant, Sussex University; p.76: Camera Press (photo: John Bulmer); p.77: Camera Press (photo: Orion Press, Tokyo); p.78: Siemens, West Germany; p.80 *top* and *bottom*: Professor R.G. Rhodes, Warwick University; p.81 *top*: Bliss Pendair Ltd; p.81 *bottom*: British Hovercraft Corporation; p.82: Submerged Buoyant Structures Ltd; p.83: Boeing Marine Systems, U.S.A.; p.84: British Aerospace; p.85: Camera Press (photo: Ray Hamilton); p.86: Dowty Group; p.87: R.M. Willoughby, International Sailiners; p.89: Ministry of Defence, London; p.91 *top* and *bottom*: Hughes Aircraft Company, U.S.A.; p.92 *top*: Science Photo Library/Rockwell; p.92 *bottom*: Mat Irvine/NASA; p.93 *top*: Rockwell; p.93 *bottom*: E.S.A.; p.94 *top* and *bottom*: Mat Irvine/NASA; p.95: E.S.A.; p.98: NASA; p.99: Mat Irvine; p.100 *top*: Space Frontiers Ltd; p.100 *bottom*: Science Photo Library/NASA; p.101: Mat Irvine/NASA; p.102: Mat Irvine/NASA; p.104: Boeing Aerospace; p.105: Boeing Aerospace; p.106: Science Photo Library/NASA; p.107: Mat Irvine/NASA; p.110: Mat Irvine/NASA; p.111: Mat Irvine/NASA; p.113 *top*: Bruce Coleman Ltd. (photo: Nicholas Devore); p.113 *bottom*: International Rice Research Institute, Phillipines; p.114: Richard Darby, National Vegetable Research Station; p.115 *top*: FAO Photo Library, Italy; p.115 *bottom*: John Innes Institute; p.116: Bruce Coleman Ltd. (photo: Timothy O'Keefe); p.117 *left* and *right*: Amchem Products Inc., U.S.A.; p.118: East Malling Research Station; p.119: Bruce Coleman Ltd. (photo: Jane Burton); p.120: Heather Angel; p.121: Bruce Coleman; p.122 *top*: FAO Photo Library; p.122 *bottom*: Trevor Lewis, Rothampstead Experimental Station; p.123: Heather Angel; p.126: FAO Photo Library; p.127: British Oxygen Company; p.128 *top*: International Development Research Centre, Canada; p.128 *bottom*: Bruce Coleman Ltd. (photo: Lynn M. Stone); p.129: FAO Photo Library; p.130: Richard Darby, N.V.R.S.; p.131: Rank Hovis McDougall Research Centre; p.133 *top* and *bottom*: *Sunday Times* Photo Library (photo: Ian Yeomans); p.134: National Physical Laboratory (Crown copyright); p.135: University of Utah, U.S.A.; p.136: EMI Medical; p.137: EMI Medical; p.138 *top*: EMI Medical; p.138 *bottom*: Camera Press (photo: Rolf Schuerch); p.139: EMI Medical; p.140: *Daily Telegraph* Colour Library; p.141: *Daily Telegraph* Colour Library; p.142: D.D. Vonberg, MRC Cyclotron Unit, Hammersmith Hospital; p.143: EMI Medical; p.144 *top, centre* and *bottom*: EMI Medical; p.145 *top* and *bottom*: E.M. Fazio, Hammersmith Hospital; p.148: D. Nicholas, Royal Marsden Hospital; p.149: Bell Laboratories; p.150: Radcliffe Infirmary; p.151: Richard and Sally Greenhill; p.152: Laser Industries Ltd., Israel.

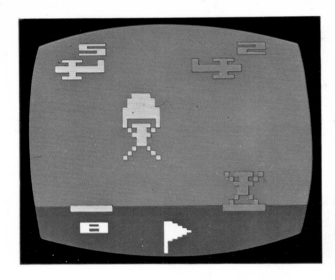

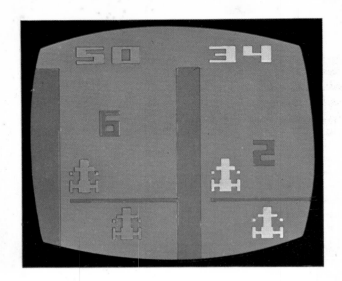

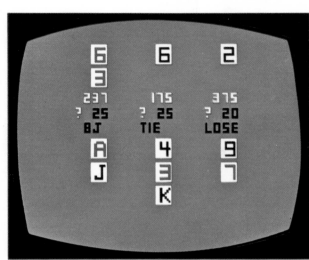

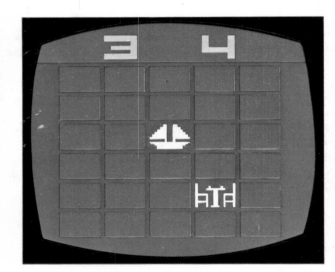

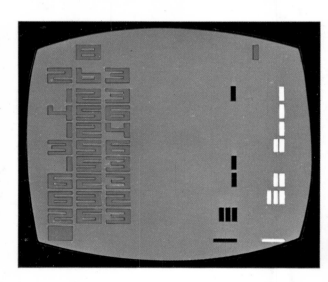

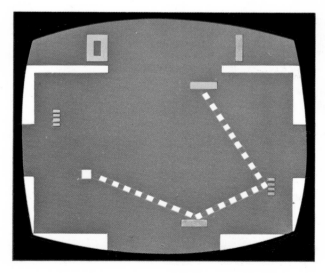

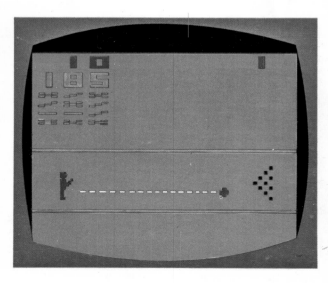